ANNELIDS

BIOLOGICAL SCIENCES

Editor

PROFESSOR H. MUNRO FOX

M.A., F.R.S.

*Emeritus Professor of Zoology
in the University of London*

ANNELIDS

R. PHILLIPS DALES

Lecturer in Zoology at Bedford College
University of London

HUTCHINSON UNIVERSITY LIBRARY
LONDON

HUTCHINSON & CO. (*Publishers*) LTD
178–202 Great Portland Street, London W.1

London Melbourne Sydney
Auckland Bombay Toronto
Johannesburg New York

★

First published 1963

595.14
DAL

*This book has been set in Times New Roman type
face. It has been printed in Great Britain by The
Anchor Press, Ltd., in Tiptree, Essex, on Smooth
Wove paper.*

CONTENTS

CONTENTS

Je dédie ce livre à la mémoire de
Pierre Fauvel avec mes hommages respectueux

ACKNOWLEDGMENTS

In the preparation of this book I have been indebted to Professor H. Munro Fox, F.R.S., for his constant encouragement, and to Dr J. Green, Professor G. E. Newell, Dr G. Parry Howells, Dr A. J. Pontin, Professor J. E. Smith, F.R.S., and Dr D. P. Wilson for their most helpful criticisms of different chapters. I should also like to thank the following for permission to make use of copyright material: Professor M. Durchon for Fig. 17E; Dr Jean Hanson for Fig. 11; Mme H. Herlant-Meewis for Fig. 18; Dr J. A. C. Nicol for Fig. 14; Professor J. E. Smith for Fig. 15; Professor G. Thorson for Fig. 17A; the Council of the Marine Biological Association of the United Kingdom for Figs 6 and 16; the Editor of the *Proceedings* of the Zoological Society of London for Fig. 9; and the Editors of the *Quarterly Journal of Microscopical Science* for Figs 3 and 4.

'Slow, soft, expanding, tenacious of life, sometimes capable of being new formed from a part, the enliveners of wet places . . .'

THOMAS PENNANT in
British Zoology, 1777

INTRODUCTION

THE earthworms are perhaps the most familiar annelids. Their bodies are long, cylindrical and annulated. Each annulus bears a series of short bristles or chaetae which can be thrust in and out to grip the soil as they burrow. Not all annelids are like this. The earthworms belong to the class Oligochaeta in which the chaetae are borne singly. In the polychaetes, as their name implies, a sheaf of chaetae arises from each chaetal sac, whilst in the leeches no chaetae are to be found.

The oligochaetes include all the earthworms together with a number of small worms found in fresh water and in estuaries. Most of them have annulated, cylindrical bodies, but some of those found in fresh water have gills and sheaves of chaetae so that they may be mistaken for polychaetes. The polychaetes are almost exclusively marine, though some are found in estuaries and a few in fresh water. They are a much larger and more varied group than the oligochaetes, for over 5,300 species have been described. There are about 3,000 known species of oligochaetes, and although varying in length from a fraction of an inch to over six feet, many are superficially similar. A few polychaetes are like earthworms, but many more have a distinct head or prostomium bearing eyes and tentacles, and have in each annulus a pair of muscular foot-like parapodia from which the bundles of chaetae protrude. Others have become adapted to living in burrows or in tubes which they construct. With loss of motility we find more selective methods of feeding, this evolution culminating in the filter-feeding fan or feather-duster worms in which the head is expanded into a brightly coloured crown.

The leeches form a more uniform group, in which 300 species are known. They are easily recognized by their suckers, the posterior one at least being well developed. Like the oligochaetes from which they are derived, the leeches are a predominantly freshwater group, though some may be found on fishes in the sea and others in moist soil, or on foliage in the tropics. Both the oligochaetes and the leeches have specialized reproductive systems; both are hermaphrodite and cross-fertilize each other—habits which have arisen in adaptation to their freshwater or semi-terrestrial life. The polychaetes, on the contrary, are typically dioecious, the gametes being shed and the larvae developing freely in the sea or in the mud in which the adults live.

There are thus three main classes of the phylum Annelida: the Polychaeta, the Oligochaeta and the leeches or Hirudinea. To these may be added two minor, but interesting, classes: the Archiannelida and the Myzostomaria. The first includes a series of genera, some of which may be survivals of the earliest annelids. They are mostly very small creatures found in surface mud and in splash pools near high-water mark. The Myzostomaria are a highly specialized group of parasites found on crinoids and in brittle-stars, some causing the formation of tumours on their hosts. Most are small, flattened and often scale-like animals, and when adult their annelid nature would hardly be suspected.

It is not the purpose of this book to present a detailed systematic account of the annelids, for this may be found in Grassé,[67] but it may not perhaps be out of place briefly to review here the different kinds of animal the phylum contains, before comparing their structure and physiology.

Many polychaetes burrow in sand and mud between tidemarks, and the most familiar are probably those dug as bait for fish: the ragworms (*Nereis*) and the lob- or lugworms (*Arenicola*). *Nereis* has a long body composed of a series of similar segments each bearing a pair of lateral parapodia. In some species these are strongly lobed, the most dorsal leaf-like lobe lying over the back. The head or prostomium bears dorsally two pairs of eyes, a pair of anterior tentacles or antennae and a pair of stout palps beneath. The two most anterior segments immediately behind the prostomium are fused to form a 'peristomium' around the mouth. The peristomium bears four pairs of tentacles or cirri derived from the reduced parapodia of these segments. Most nereids live in burrows, but they may crawl from the burrow openings to feed on the surface, and may swim after a fashion when covered by the tide. *Arenicola* is relatively helpless on the surface of the mud, but will bury itself again when dug up. Its more cylindrical, plump body, reduced parapodia and simple prostomium fit it for a burrowing life.

Most polychaetes are either adapted for an active life, when the prostomium and parapodia are well developed, as in *Nereis*, or for a life in a burrow or tube, when the body is commonly cylindrical, the parapodia reduced and the prostomium simple and devoid of appendages, as in *Arenicola*. The Polychaeta are, indeed, most usually divided into two subclasses, the Errantia and the Sedentaria. This division is not a natural one, however, and does not reflect the way in which these worms have evolved, a subject discussed in chapter 3.

Other common polychaetes of the 'errant' type are the green or brown phyllodocids often found in crevices or under boulders on the shore. They have well-developed eyes on the prostomium, tentacles, and parapodia which bear leafy lobes over the back. Eyes are very much larger in the pelagic, transparent alciopids, otherwise very like the phyllodocids from which they are derived. *Nephthys*, another 'errant' worm, may also be encountered on sandy shores. It is an almost colourless, pearly worm which swims vigorously if dug up and thrown back into the sea. While the parapodia are well developed it can burrow rapidly. It has a relatively small prostomium, and indeed it is difficult on first acquaintance to tell which end is which. There are many smaller worms with well-developed parapodia and

tentacles found under stones and amongst weed. Some of
the largest, on the other hand, are the 'rockworms' belonging to the family Eunicidae. Superficially like nereids, but
of very different ancestry, these worms differ in the number
of head tentacles, in the shape of the parapodial lobes and
in the kinds of chaetae they bear. There is one further group
of worms often encountered under stones on the sea-shore,
which is placed in the 'Errantia'. These are the scaleworms,
so called from the scale-like disc-shaped growths from
certain of the parapodia which may overlap one another
over the back. Fauvel[55] included all of them within the
family Aphroditidae, which he divided into a series of
subfamilies. Most taxonomists now elevate these subfamilies to family status, so that the Aphroditidae include
only the 'sea-mice' *Aphrodite* and *Hermione*, in which the
scales are covered—or partly covered—by a mat of hair-like
chaetae. The sea-mice are found below low-water mark
scuttling over, or burrowing just below, the surface of the
sand. The remaining families are referred to as 'scaleworms',
for the scales are readily seen on the back. They are found
in a variety of places: under stones, in shells, in the burrows
of other annelids and on echinoderms.

A great variety of polychaetes have become sedentary in
habit. Mention has already been made of the lugworm
Arenicola, and there are many others that live in temporary
burrows in the sand and mud which they eat. Capitellids
and ariciids are small, elongate, usually thread-like, blood-
red worms often seen when digging for rag- or lugworms.
The opheliids are less often seen, but are similarly adapted
for burrowing in that each has a simple, conical prostomium
and a fusiform body. *Glycera* has a similarly pointed prostomium and a long, muscular, tubular body. When dug
out of the mud in which it lives, the body is lashed about,
coiling and uncoiling. Some relatives of the eunicid rockworms, the arabellids and lumbrinereids, are surprisingly
like earthworms; they are often found in the holdfasts of
large algae and amongst the roots of eelgrass.

Other polychaetes live in permanent burrows or tubes

which they secrete or build from gathered materials and which they may never leave. Because of this, various modifications are found for feeding, for obtaining oxygen and for clearing away excretory waste. Whilst the problems of living permanently in a tube and the ways in which they have been solved by annelids are discussed in later chapters, we may note here two main tendencies. First, an evolution of feeding tentacles capable of extension from the tube, and, secondly, of the formation of gills which may either be protruded from the tube opening or are irrigated by water passed through the tube by activity of the worm. These two developments account for many of the more obvious differences between the 'errant' and 'sedentary' types of polychaete: a description of the former will be found in chapter 2, that of the latter in chapter 4. The most specialized tube-dwellers are the sabellid and serpulid fan-worms which extend their feathery crowns into open water for purposes both of feeding and of respiration. The serpulids may be recognized by their limy tubes and by the adaptation, in most of them, of one of the rays of the crown as an operculum which acts as a stopper to the tube when the worm retracts. Serpulid tubes may be found on stones, empty shells or old bottles fished up from deep water; a few smaller ones may be found on fronds of sea-weed. The more familiar tentacle-feeders include the terebellids, which have a mass of extensile tentacles arising medusa-like from the prostomium. Most are found in mud or under large stones. There are many other groups which have developed tentacles for feeding and to which we shall refer in more detail in chapter 2.

On turning to the oligochaetes we find far less variety in external appearance. But what the group may lack in variety is made up for in abundance. The bottoms of ponds and lakes may contain enormous numbers of small oligochaetes; over 40,000 have been counted in spring from a square metre at the bottom of the lake in Regent's Park, London. The earthworms are all cylindrical, evenly seg-mented animals, and whilst there are many species these are not all easily distinguished. Nevertheless, there are often more differences in internal structure between genera, at least, than their external appearance would suggest, especially with regard to the arrangement of the reproductive and excretory organs. Perhaps the most familiar freshwater oligochaete is *Tubifex*, a bright red, cylindrical worm, in which the hind end of the body writhes above the mud where it lives. It is the 'blood-worm' which can be bought by the sixpennyworth from aquarists' shops. Characteristic of foul conditions, the blood-red colour of countless millions may be seen on the Thames mud of central London at low tide in summer. Some of the most interesting oligochaetes, such as *Aelosoma*, *Stylaria* and *Chaetogaster*, may best be seen by examining, with the aid of a lens, silt from the bottom of ponds and streams allowed to settle in a dish. These small worms are mostly predators or scavengers living on other small creatures or their remains in the detritus. They have tactile prostomiums and often look more like polychaetes than oligochaetes for their chaetae are arranged in bundles.

Many leeches too are common in ponds and ditches: most are predators, and a few are parasites. Leeches are easily recognized by the large and often disc-shaped posterior sucker. The region around the mouth is not always elaborated into as prominent a sucker as the posterior one, but many fish leeches or Piscicolidae have large disc-shaped anterior as well as posterior suckers, perhaps to hold on to their slippery, fast-moving prey. Leeches vary a lot in size, most of those common in our ponds and streams are quite small; others such as *Trocheta*, a predator of earthworms found in moist soil, may be several inches long—as big as a medicinal leech. In South America, or in the tropics of the Old World, leeches are found six inches or more in length. The body surface is usually much annulated and somewhat repellently formless. The piscicolids are rather different in these respects, for they are often warty in appearance, and some such as *Branchellion* have a series of paired gills.

These, then, are the animals with which we are concerned

in these pages. They are all soft-bodied creatures without any hard skeletal structures, for while the epidermis secretes a thin cuticle, this is pliant and non-supporting. Their bodies are essentially cylinders of muscle arranged in segmental units, enclosing a fluid-filled cavity, the coelom. Beneath the epidermis is a layer of circular muscle, and beneath this a layer of longitudinally directed muscles. These circular and longitudinal muscle layers are antagonistic because the coelomic fluid is incompressible, for contraction of one causes deformation of the other; the coelom is said to act as a hydrostatic skeleton. The series of segments of which the annelid body is composed is bounded by the anterior prostomium and the posterior pygidium.

These general features of the annelid body—the hydrostatic skeleton, the muscular system derived from the segmented mesoderm, the embryological origin of the mesoderm and of the coelom contained within it, the relation of the coelom to the outside by the segmental ducts and nephridia, and the constitution of the prostomium—are subjects described in chapter 1. The chapters that follow are concerned, in a comparative way, with the gut and feeding mechanisms, the vascular system and respiration, excretion, the nervous system and co-ordination of movement, the sense organs and behaviour, and the reproductive methods and development of annelids. The way in which the main classes have evolved is discussed in two further chapters: the evolution and classification of the polychaetes in chapter 3, the oligochaetes and leeches in chapter 9. A complete classification of the Annelida, together with the names of all the genera mentioned throughout the book, is given in the Appendix. Space has allowed quotation of only a few of the many publications in which the reader may find in more detail subjects only briefly mentioned here, but many of those included in the list of references at the end of this book have been selected for the useful bibliographies they themselves contain.

1

THE GENERAL ORGANIZATION OF
THE ANNELID BODY

THE ancestral annelids may be imagined to have had a body composed of a series of annuli or segments, each enclosing a similar complement of organ systems. None of the annelids alive today conforms to such a simple plan, though many, such as *Nereis diversicolor*, the common ragworm of our shores, have long series of segments with an essentially similar construction. Each segment comprises an outer layer of circular muscle underlying a thin cuticle and epidermis, and an inner system of longitudinal muscle blocks. Both circular and longitudinal muscle layers are syncytial tissues. In earthworms the longitudinal muscles are strengthened by collagenous lamellae, giving character-istic feather-like patterns in cross-section. The leeches have an additional double layer of muscles between the outer circulars and inner longitudinals, directed diagonally in both directions across the longitudinal axis of the body (fig. 1). Each component of this double layer spirals round the body in a continuous geodetic helix.[108] Leeches also have muscles running from the dorsal to the ventral side of the body in each segment.

The cuticle, in earthworms at least, is mainly a collagen-ous protein plus a polysaccharide (giving galactose on hydrolysis) and a small gelatin fraction.[140, 159] The chaetae which are secreted from epidermal inpushings are different. Bobin and Mazoué[13] found that those of the polychaete *Aphrodite* are made of fibrillae of chitin held together by scleroprotein. Lotmar and Picken[101] have confirmed that the chaetae consist of chitin, and have shown that this is in a slightly different form from that in arthropods. All chaetae give positive chitosan reactions. The secretion of chaetae has been much studied by Bobin.[12]

The gut is separated from the muscles of the body wall by a fluid-filled space, the coelom, which is bounded on all surfaces by the peritoneum. The coelom leads to the outside in each segment by a pair of coelomoducts, and by a pair of nephridia, or by structures derived from their combination.

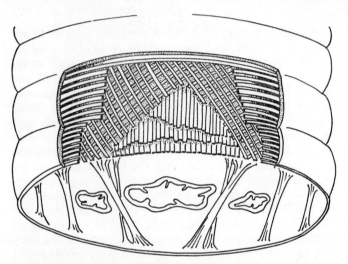

Fig.1. The muscular system of the leech *Poecilobdella* (redrawn after Bhatia[6]). The muscles shown are those in the 3rd and 4th annuli of a segment from the middle region of the body

Two systems, apart from the gut, link the segments into a functional whole: the vascular system, and the nervous system. The vascular system commonly consists of a dorsal vessel conveying the blood forwards, and a ventral longitudinal vessel which conveys the blood in the opposite direction, joined by vessels to the gut and body wall completing the circuit in each segment. The nervous system is represented by an invariably ventral and solid nerve cord from which lateral nerves arise in each segment. The nerve cord may be single or consist of two strands, usually bound together, but sometimes remaining separate.

Every segment arises as a unit, emphasized by the provision of a membranous septum separating one from another, but each has little autonomy. Growth leading to a multiplication of segmental units results in a certain monotony of structure. In polychaetes each segment bears a pair of lateral parapodia from which the chaetae arise. In some polychaetes the parapodia are uniramous, but in most they are bilobed, with a bundle of chaetae emerging from the dorsal notopodium, and another bundle emerging from the ventral neuropodium. There is also a single heavy chaeta or aciculum supporting each bundle, and muscles arising from the body wall are attached to its base. By their contraction the whole chaetal bundle may be thrust out. The parapodium is moved to and fro by other muscles arising from different parts of the body wall, and may bear sensory cirri, gills or lobes protecting the body.

In annelids the segments are essentially muscular units, and their repetition is associated with locomotory patterns. In worms which are sedentary or burrow by a peristaltic movement, this segmental plan may be modified. The most obvious differences amongst active annelids which crawl or swim are related to structures that do not interfere with the segmental arrangement of the body muscles. The morphological variations within the Annelida demonstrate what has so far been achieved within the confines of a segmental body plan, without the aid of a hard skeleton. It is of some interest, therefore, to know how segmentation arose.

Origin of the coelom and mesoderm

It has been suggested that the serial repetition of paired reproductive organs seen in some nemertines and flatworms was the first step towards a segmented structure. According to this theory, which has wide acceptance today, the enlargement of such a series of paired gonads had a double effect: first it tended to isolate the longitudinal muscles between each pair of gonads, and secondly the cavities of the gonads became greatly enlarged to form the coelom; their ducts, the coelomoducts. The enlargement of the coelomic spaces may also have been connected with the need for control of osmotic inflow of water. This 'gonocoel' theory of the origin of the coelom was first put forward by Hatschek in 1878 and extended later by Goodrich.[66]

In annelids the fertilized egg first divides into two, and then into four, cells by vertical (meridional) total cleavages almost at right angles to one another. These four cells are somewhat unequal in size, and may be labelled A, B, C and D in a clockwise direction as viewed from the top or the end which will become anterior. These four blastomeres, of which D is the largest, then divide simultaneously, somewhat obliquely and above the equator, to give eight cells—a quartette of smaller cells or micromeres above (1a, 1b, 1c, 1d) and a quartette of megameres (1A, 1B, 1C, 1D) below (fig. 2A). At the following division all eight cells again divide simultaneously; the megameres giving off another quartette of micromeres (2a, 2b, 2c, 2d), themselves becoming 2A, 2B, 2C and 2D, and the first quartette of micromeres dividing to become $1a^1$–$1d^1$ and $1a^2$–$1d^2$ (fig. 2B). Simultaneous divisions of all these cells follow, though the megameres begin to lag behind the divisions of the micromeres which tend to overgrow them to form a morula. The division of each quartette is oblique, daughter cells being dealt by the megameres alternately to the right and to the left (fig. 2C). This method of cleavage is referred to as spiral. The origin of the primary germ layers may be traced from the 64-cell stage (fig. 2D). By then the first three quartettes of micromeres have been cut off and these with their own offspring give rise to the whole of the ectoderm and the mesenchymal cells which wander inwards, the ectomesoderm. 3A–3C, and 4D give rise to the endoderm. The mesoderm which forms the muscles and in which the coelomic sacs arise is formed entirely from 4d. The

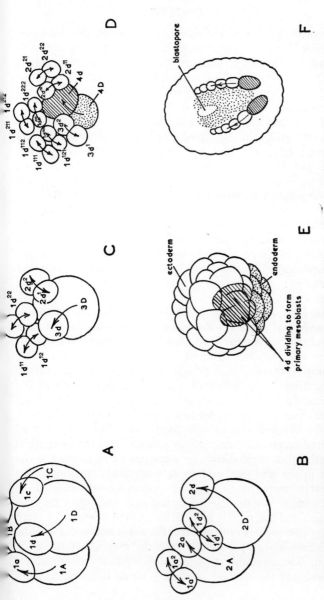

FIG. 2. Diagrams illustrating the origin of the mesoderm in annelids: A, 8-cell stage; B, 16-cell stage (only the descendants of cells A and D are shown); C, D, 32-cell and 64-cell stages (showing only the descendants of cell D); E, appearance of the morula after the 64-cell stage, the primary mesoblasts (hatched), being overgrown by ectoderm (unshaded), endoderm (stippled); F, mesoderm cells being proliferated forward from the primary mesoblasts

repeated division of the megameres reduces the difference in size between the daughter cells, and in the fourth quartette 4d may actually be larger than its parent megamere (fig. 2D). Of this fourth quartette, 4a–4c are added to megameres forming the endoderm of the larval archenteron and the gut wall of the adult worm. The endodermal cells are brought into an internal position in the embryo by the continued division and subsequent overgrowth by the earlier micromeres and by invagination (fig. 2E). The resulting blastopore constricts in the middle, and the mouth is formed by a further stomodeal ingrowth of ectodermal micromeres at its anterior end (fig. 2F).

The fate of the cells resulting from spiral cleavage is different in some leeches, and in some oligochaetes the divisions of each quartette may get out of step, giving a slightly different pattern. In glossiphoniid leeches the mesoderm is derived from both 4d and 4D, so that the endoderm receives no contribution from the fourth quartette.

By forward proliferation of the mesoblast cells a band of mesodermal tissue is established on each side. Within each band cavities appear, and each pair of cavities enlarges to form the coelomic space of a single segment in the adult worm. As the mesoblast cells arise posteriorly and pay off the mesodermal cells forwards, the most anterior parts of the mesoderm and their coelomic cavities are the oldest. Such continued growth establishes a body consisting of a long series of similar segments composed of a succession of paired coelomic sacs which eventually become almost confluent, separated only by a suspensory membrane of the gut in the mid-line, and by thin membranous septa. The median membranes may be perforated or reduced to occasional suspensory ligaments, and the septa may be obliterated completely in some specialized worms. The inner layer of mesoderm surrounding the gut is elaborated into the gut musculature; the outer into the muscles of the body wall. The coelomic sacs acquire separate coelomoducts opening to the outside, so there is a pair in every segment.

The vascular system, including a sinus or capillary network surrounding the gut, is also entirely mesodermal in origin —a topic once the subject of much debate, discussed by Hanson.[73]

Whatever the factors involved in the origin of the coelom may have been, and whatever the original relationship of these spaces to the gonads, the provision of a series of paired sacs on each side of the gut had obvious advantages. In the first place the gut, separated from the body wall with its own muscles, could move independently, and this led to further differentiation. The coelom itself provided not only a space in which the gametes could mature, but one in which food substances and excretory products could be transported or stored. It also provided a hydrostatic skeleton on which the muscles could act. The acquisition of a coelomic space, whilst revealing these possibilities, did not, however, avoid presenting some problems. The most obvious of these was that the gut was no longer close to the muscles of the body wall where much of the worm's energy is expended, and was farther from the surface where respiratory exchange could occur. The development of a coelom was therefore concomitant with the evolution of a blood vascular system to transport nutrients from the gut to the body wall, and to transport respiratory gases to and from the surface.

The prostomium

It will be recalled that the mesoderm is proliferated from a pair of posterior mesoblasts, and that the coelomic spaces of each segment are derived from cavities which appear in the bands so formed. This leaves an anterior presegmental region which is incorporated in the head or prostomium of the adult, and a similar postsegmental part, the pygidium. Although the prostomium is partly, if not wholly, presegmental, the mesodermal bands commonly grow forward into this region on each side to fuse in front of the mouth, and paired sacs may arise within them. In *Serpula* there is a single pair of preoral coelomic sacs; in the ariciid,

Scoloplos, Anderson[4] has found three; but in *Owenia* there are none.[171] Some morphologists have maintained that the occurrence of these sacs lends support to the view that the prostomium is derived from a number of segments which have been reduced by cephalization. The suggestion that the prostomium might contain as many as three segments first came from the studies of the brain, which in many worms gives the appearance of being made up of three pairs of ganglia closely fused, a view held by Nilsson. Opponents of this idea argued that the brain is functionally separable into 'fore', 'mid' and 'hind' brain regions owing to the correlation centres associated with the paired sense organs which are borne on the prostomium. These are the tactile and possibly chemosensory antennae and palps, the eyes, and the chemosensory nuchal organs, none of which has any obvious counterpart on the succeeding segments. Hanström[75] interpreted the most anterior part of the brain as a later addition representing the ganglia of the first segment.

Anderson's[4] elegant study of the development of *Scoloplos* contains the most recent review of this subject. He concluded that there was no evidence for the view that there are vestiges of any segments in front of the first definitive trunk segment; that the brain and the circumoesophageal commissures are presegmental structures, and that the forward growth of the mesoderm and the appearance of cavities within it are secondary developments. The fate of the cells in the anterior region is also complicated by the elaboration of larval tissue which is lost on the assumption of the adult structure. A simplified ciliated trochophore larva is formed, at first bearing a single trochus or belt of cilia just above the equator, and later an additional, though smaller, band or telotroch round the anus. Anderson emphasized that the descendants of the first quartette of micromeres give rise to the whole of the brain and the ectoderm of the upper half of the trochophore ($1a^1$–$1d^1$), including the prototroch ($1a^2$–$1d^2$), and form all the ectodermal tissue of the adult prostomium in every polychaete in which the development is sufficiently known. Immediately behind the prototroch the ectoderm of the mouth region is formed from descendants of 2d, and is thus also presegmental. The circumoesophageal commissures then grow down from the developing brain to meet the ventral ganglia in the first trunk segment behind the oral tissue. In the elaborate trochophores of serpulids much of the ectoderm above the prototroch is lost, and in *Owenia*[171] and *Polygordius*,[174] whose specialized larvae necessitate a cataclysmic metamorphosis to attain the adult form, much of the ectoderm of the lower part of the trochophore is also lost. Those cells which do remain from this region form the ectoderm round the mouth, but this is more easily seen in worms with yolky eggs in which the trochophore stage tends to be suppressed.

From this it would appear that not only is the prostomium a presegmental structure, but that the tissues surrounding and immediately behind the mouth are also presegmental in origin. The most anterior segment is commonly fused to this buccal region to form what is usually referred to as the peristomium or 'buccal segment' in polychaetes, and further anterior segments may be added in some worms. The muscles of the mouth region are derived from the forward extension of the mesodermal bands on each side, and while the coelomic sacs may be formed in them, no segmentation is induced in the overlying ectoderm. The peristomium of *Nereis* is formed by a fusion of two trunk segments, as it bears two pairs of cirri on each side similar to those of the parapodia farther back. The more posterior of these cirral pairs is innervated by a parapodial ganglion just beneath the bases of the cirri, and secondarily connected to another ganglion on the circumoesophageal commissure at the same horizontal level. The development of the brain and the anterior nervous system of *Nereis* has been reinvestigated by Gilpin-Brown,[65] and it is clear that the degree of cephalization is variable even from one species to another within the genus. But in every instance the ganglia of these cephalized segments remain distinct from the brain, even when their individuality is externally masked by a loss of their parapodia in the adult worm. Certainly Clark's[24] studies of the internal structure of the brain of both *Nereis* and *Nephthys* do not suggest that the brain is formed from fused segmental ganglia. Larval development in polychaetes has itself been subject to evolution, and it is impossible to determine whether the forward growth of the mesodermal bands and the formation of paired sacs within them are indicative of a more extensive segmentation in a remote ancestor, or due to specialization. We can at present only conclude that there is certainly no evidence whatever for the view that any part of the brain, circumoesophageal commissures or the mouth region is derived from the most anterior segments by cephalization, and that on the contrary the brain and all the structures that it directly innervates, such as the palps and antennae, are presegmental in nature. Structures such as the peristomial cirri, which are manifestly derived from the most anterior segments, are always innervated from ganglia which retain their identity and remain separate from the brain.

The brain shifts backward in both the earthworms and the leeches with the increasing loss of functional identity of the prostomium, in earthworms in relation to the conically pointed and muscular anterior region required for burrowing, and in leeches in connexion with the development of an anterior sucker round the mouth. In leeches, indeed, the prostomium is very small and many of the paired anterior sense organs are no longer borne by it but by the most anterior segments. In the horse leech, *Haemopis*, the brain lies at the back of the seventh segment, but the segmental nerves innervating the segments in front arise from the circumoesophageal commissures and all retain their identity.[108]

Just as the anterior end of the body is formed from a presegmental region, so the posterior end is postsegmental and forms the pygidium. Like the prostomium, its ectoderm is derived early in development from cells arising during closure of the blastopore; in all worms studied in sufficient detail, it has been found that the pygidial ectoderm is derived from 2d, which also gives rise to the telotroch of the trochophore. If the pygidium contains any mesoderm at all, this is derived by backward extension of the mesoderm from the last segment, just as the prostomial mesoderm is derived by a forward extension from the first. In the adult the pygidium is usually small, though it may bear a pair of sensory cirri as in *Nereis*, a ring of cirri as in the maldanid (bamboo) worms, or even a pair of eyespots as in some small sabellids such as *Fabricia*.

The nephridia and coelomoducts

The coelom is connected to the outside not only by the coelomoducts but by the nephridia. The two structures are often intimately related, a circumstance which formed the subject of much study by Goodrich.[66] The first nephridia to arise in the developing larva each consists of a few syncytial cells with an intracellular blind-ending tubule containing a terminal flagellum and draining to the outside. Such solenocytes are always the first to be formed in the larva, whatever the nephridia of the adult may be like. In many polychaetes the adult nephridia consist of bunches of solenocytes joined to a common duct passing through the septum to open to the outside from the next segment. Such protonephridia, as they are called, are found in phyllodocids and in the sand-burrowing nephthyids where solenocytes were first discovered in annelids by Goodrich. In many other polychaetes, on the other hand, and in oligochaetes and leeches, an open funnel or nephridiostome is formed. In the larvae of *Perinereis cultrifera* these are formed directly from closed protonephridia. The first pairs of nephridia in the third and fourth segments of a six- to eight-segmented larva develop as protonephridia which acquire a pore near the tip projecting into the coelom, this pore being then elaborated into the ciliated funnel of the adult nephridium. Such open nephridia, or metanephridia as they are called, are found not only in nereids, but also in capitellid polychaetes. In capitellids the metanephridia and the coelomoducts are separate, the coelomoducts in the segments in which gametes are produced having large ciliated funnels acting as separate gonoducts. In other polychaetes the coelomoducts may be grafted on to the stem of the nephridium to form a nephromixium, which may be used both as a genital and as an excretory duct. The ciliated funnel of the coelomoduct may come to open into the side of the nephridial canal when this leads from closed solenocytes, and such proto-nephromixia are found in the phyllodocids, alciopids and glycerids. When the nephridium is a metanephridium, the coelomostome may be grafted directly on to the nephridiostome forming a mixonephridium, which may then have a larger, more flared, ciliated funnel. In some instances the nephridiostome remains as a recognizable notch or pocket in the larger coelomostome, as it does, for example, in some syllids. In others, the original nephridiostome is completely replaced, so that its true nature is revealed only in development. This grafting of the coelomostome on to the nephridiostome may occur only on reaching sexual maturity, or only in those segments in which the gametes arise. Sometimes all the main nephridia may be permanently of this nature, as they are in the lugworm, *Arenicola marina*.

The association between the nephridia and the coelomostomes may become further specialized in relation to the gametes. In male alciopids, for example, which have proto-nephridia, the coelomostomes take up the whole of the sperm produced in the segment like a cloak, and form globular seminal vesicles in which the sperm are kept until shed. Similar sperm sacs are formed in some syllids, though in them the nephridia are metanephridia, not protonephridia. Many polychaetes have abandoned the habit of shedding the sperm or eggs through the coelomoducts or nephridia, and have adopted the more drastic measure of allowing the gametes to escape by rupture of the body wall or gut. In them the coelomostome is usually retained as a ciliated flap or patch on the peritoneum or on the side of the nephridium, without opening into its duct. In nereids these ciliated patches may be seen on the ventral edges of the dorsal longitudinal muscle blocks in the mid-body region; in nephthyids they form large ridged flaps

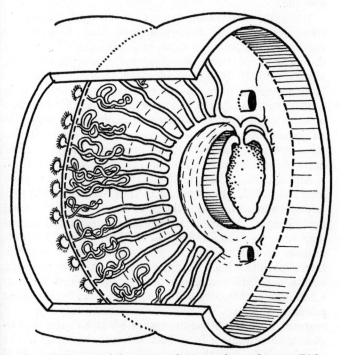

FIG. 3. Enteronephric system of *Megascolex cochinensis* (74th segment). Redrawn from Bahl[6]

or pockets on the stems of the protonephridia. Steps in this remarkable conversion of the coelomostome may be seen in different hesionid polychaetes. In *Irma* there are mixonephridia serving both as excretory and as genital ducts, the coelomostomes being completely confluent with the nephridiostomes. In *Ophiodromus* the coelomostome forms a sort of cowl somewhat to one side of the nephridiostome, whilst in *Hesione* the coelomostome takes the form of a large crescentic fold attached to the stem of the nephridium just below the completely separate nephridiostome.

While the coelomoducts may be primarily segmental structures, and the nephridia have had a segmental metamerism imposed on them, multiple ducts or nephridia do occur in some annelids. *Nephthys ciliata*, for example, has chains of 10–16 ciliated organs on each side in the midbody segments; there are several pairs of nephromixia in each segment in *Glycera*, and there is a similar multiplication in some capitellids. In polychaetes nephromixia may also be joined from segment to segment, or some anterior mixonephridia may be greatly enlarged. Large anterior nephridia are found in cirratulids, terebellids and sabellids.

All oligochaetes have metanephridia. The tubule is often long and coiled, and may show definite regions leading to a terminal bladder or vesicle closed by means of a sphinctered nephridiopore. In some earthworms the nephridial system may be more complicated. The original pair of nephridioblasts may subdivide to give a number of separate meronephridia.[6] Each meronephridium may be provided with a nephridiostome, and their tubules joined to form a common duct leading to the nephridiopore. In *Pheretima posthuma* there are 40–50 of these meronephridia in each segment from the fifteenth septum backward, the nephridiostomes projecting from both sides of the septum. The septal ducts from all these nephridia empty into longitudinal channels running along the dorsal side of the gut. These open, not to the outside, but into the lumen of the gut at each septum. This meronephridial system draining to the gut rather than directly to the outside is seen in other earthworms with many variations in the detail of the draining ducts (fig. 3). In *Tonoscolex*, for example, the nephridiostomes are all on the anterior face of the septum, and form two groups opening separately by a pair of pores into the gut

in each segment. Meronephridia may also lack nephridiostomes, closing over completely. In *Hoplochaetella* there
are, in addition to a pair of ordinary nephridia in each
segment, dozens of very small 'micronephridia' scattered
over the body wall, each opening to the outside by a
separate pore.

In the oligochaetes the nephridial tissue would seem to
be exceptionally plastic, and in some genera all variations
in relationship or division may be found in the same animal.
In *Eutyphoeus*, for example, some septal and integumentary

FIG. 4. Multiple non-functional nephridiostomes in *Hoplochaetella khandalensis*. Redrawn from Bahl[6]

meronephridia drain directly to the outside, while others
drain forwards into the pharynx. In *Thamnodrilus crassus*
the nephridia are normal in the sense that there is a single
pair which drain to the outside in each segment, but these
open into the coelom by multiple funnels, about 45 minute
copies leading to each duct. Multiple funnels are found also
in *Hoplochaetella khandalensis*, but these are not open
(fig. 4). Integumentary meronephridia are generally small
and secondarily closed, as are those which drain into the
pharynx and buccal cavity; those borne on septa, whether
subdivided, enteronephric or leading directly to the outside
commonly retain their funnels. The enteronephric system is
apparently related to water conservation.

The genital ducts of oligochaetes are coelomoducts, and

B

with the assumption of hermaphroditism, the gonads are restricted to a few segments only. There is no relation between the coelomoducts and the nephridia. The coelomostomes are frequently large, and form elaborate funnels in those segments in which the testes lie, though in the segments containing ovaries the ducts are sometimes reduced to mere pores. In connexion with the male apertures there are often additional ectodermal invaginations fusing with the mesodermal duct or vas deferens to form accessory glands and copulatory structures; developments related to their terrestrial life and cross-fertilizing habits.

Save for multiple funnels such as are found in the nephridia of the Indian cattle leech *Poecilobdella*, the nephridial systems of leeches are usually simpler than those in some of the earthworms we have just described, though in the piscicolids the tubules are branched and connect one with another. The leeches, however, are characterized by a growth of mesenchyme restricting the coelom to a system of channels. The most obvious of these is one on each side of the body and it is into ampullae arising from them that the nephridiostomes open. The nephridiostome itself is not easily recognized as the ampulla is commonly filled with phagocytes. The nephridiostome leads into a large sac or capsule before entering the coiled tubule which is unciliated and leads separately to the outside. Just as each nephridium has a coelomic ampulla, each gonad is enclosed in a sac opening into a gonadial coelomoduct.

The hydrostatic skeleton

In all annelids the coelom acts as a hydrostatic skeleton depending on the fact that as the coelomic fluid is incompressible, contraction of any muscle causes deformation of others. Most of what we know about annelids in this respect is based on work done on the common lugworm, *Arenicola marina*, and on earthworms, which is reviewed by Chapman.[22] In the lugworm, Chapman and Newell[22] found that even when quiescent a healthy worm maintained a coelomic fluid pressure of some 14 cm of water. When anaesthetized with urethane, the pressure fell to little more than 3 cm. Clearly some of the body-wall muscles are in a state of tonus even when the worm is inactive. By passing a hypodermic needle connected to a sea-water manometer into the coelom, they found that the pressure increased to as much as 30 cm of water in the anterior end of the body when the worm burrowed. The leech *Haemadipsa* can stand erect on its posterior sucker in air, according to Stammers,[146] an ability perhaps conferred by the spiral muscles.

The virtual loss of locomotory ability when an annelid is punctured confirms the belief that the efficient working of the muscles is dependent on maintenance of a correct fluid volume. Chapman and Newell found that a loss of 0·38 ml from a full-sized lugworm more than doubled the time taken to burrow, but amputating the hinder half extended the burrowing time by only 70%, as fluid was retained by contraction of the circular muscles in front of the cut.

It may well be asked how it is that as the coelom communicates with the outside by a series of nephridia and segmental ducts, that pressure can be maintained. In earthworms there is in addition a dorsal pore in each segment providing more potential leaks. How does the worm prevent itself from leaking at a rate that would make the system unworkable?

In the first place all the ducts that have been examined are closed by sphincters, and the urine is drained only at intervals. A fully grown *Lumbricus terrestris* has some 150 segments, each with a pair of nephridia and a single dorsal pore. The worm is therefore perforated by 450 holes, each of which, nevertheless, is mostly kept closed. There have been few measurements made of the amount of fluid actually passing out of the body in such animals. Wolf[173] calculated that *Lumbricus terrestris* lost about 60% of its total weight each day as fluid, Bahl[6] that the Indian earthworm *Pheretima posthuma* lost 45% of its total weight each day, amounting to 0·3–0·4 ml/worm/hr. Ramsay[132] has collected

0·001 ml of fluid from a single nephridium of an anaesthetized *Lumbricus terrestris* in an hour, and Chapman[22] has
calculated that this would mean a total urine flow of
0·3 ml/worm/hr, a value similar to Bahl's measurement
in *Pheretima*. This flow of urine is appreciable, and to
maintain the volume and hence the pressure of the coelomic
fluid without which the animal would be immobilized, there
must be a constant replacement. The nephridia are
important not only in regulating the composition of the
body fluid, but indirectly in the maintenance of muscular
activity.

The next question is whether this flow of urine is due to
the pressure of the coelomic fluid. The nephridia are
relatively long tubes of very small bore. The rate at which
fluid may pass through a tube may be calculated when the
difference in pressure between the two ends, the length, and
the diameter are known. Chapman[22] has calculated that in
Lumbricus terrestris the nephridial length is 3·5 cm, and the
radius 0·0005–0·001 cm; Newell[115] that the average coelomic pressure in the anterior region is 16 cm of water in an
active worm. From this it may be calculated that 0·01–0·25
ml may pass in an hour. This is rather less than Ramsay's
finding. If the internal pressure is increased, then the rate of
flow will also be increased, and this increased rate of flow,
if the nephridiopores were open, would cause a significant
loss of fluid and impair the efficiency of the hydrostatic
skeleton; the sphincters are clearly important. It is not clear
what the functions of the dorsal pores are, but it may be
that they serve in keeping the skin moist for respiration
rather than as safety valves, although fluid may spurt out of
them when a worm is roughly handled. The dorsal pores
seem to be a new development in the earthworms, and are
unrelated to the coelomoducts.

The volume enclosed by the body-wall muscles acts as a
hydrostatic skeleton even when filled with free cells, gametes
or mesenchyme. The disposition and completeness of the
septa, on the other hand, are important in determining the
extent of transmission of fluid from one part of the body to

another as a result of local muscular contraction, and hence the extent of its antagonizing effect on other muscles. The septa tend to be rather complete in worms which crawl or in which the movements of each segment are independent of, or necessarily out of phase with, those adjoining. Conversely they tend to be reduced or lost where the muscles of a series of adjacent segments are co-ordinated to work together. In *Arenicola marina*, for example, three anterior septa alone remain in the main part of the body, and these tend to isolate the proboscis which might otherwise be everted by movements of the fluid in the main body cavity. In the earthworms the septa are virtually complete and Newell[115] found that there is no or little movement of fluid from one segment to the next. Each septum indeed has a complicated musculature to control bulging. This isolation of adjacent segments enables several waves of contraction in the body-wall muscles to pass down the body at the same time, and helps to establish a crawling motion. The septa are thus of great functional importance in relation to movement.

In most cylindrical animals with a hydrostatic skeleton, the body-wall muscles are differentiated into an outer layer of circular muscle and an inner layer of longitudinal muscle. The longitudinal muscles are often arranged as a series of blocks: in *Nereis* there is a dorsal pair and a ventral pair separated by the parapodial musculature; in earthworms the longitudinal muscles, though divided into bands, form a more complete cylinder. This arrangement of the muscle into circular and longitudinal layers is the only one in which each is perfectly antagonized by the other through the effect of the coelomic fluid. To appreciate this more fully, it is instructive to consider, as Chapman[22] has done, the body as a simple closed cylinder.

If such a cylinder were surrounded by circular muscles alone, contraction of these towards one end would decrease the diameter at that end resulting in a movement of fluid which could: 1, increase the length of the contracting end, the other end remaining unaltered; 2, increase the diameter of the other end, the total length remaining the same; 3, increase the length of the other end, but not its diameter; and 4, cause extension of both ends, the diameter of the non-contracting end remaining what it was. Intermediate conditions are also possible. Only in the second possibility, where the length remains unaltered, could contraction of the circular muscles at the inflated end restore the system to its original condition. Nevertheless, if longitudinal muscles were also present, the contraction of these in the other three cases could restore the cylinder to its original dimensions.

The segmental origin and arrangement of the circular and longitudinal muscles with segmental innervation from the nerve cord provides the necessary regional autonomy to enable a variety of movements to be performed. The proportion of circular to longitudinal muscle varies. The longitudinal muscles are usually better developed than the circular, for as Chapman[22] has pointed out, a given percentage change in circumference of a closed cylinder of fixed volume—which is what an annelid is—is accompanied by twice this change in length. It follows that the smaller the circumference the greater the increase in length, with a given percentage change in circumference, and conversely the greater the circumference the smaller the change in length will be. Worms which crawl about actively in and out of crevices are, therefore, likely to be best adapted if small and elongate; and worms which burrow, if they are plump. The slender and generally active phyllodocids might be regarded as examples of the first; the lugworms of the second. Again, worms which both crawl and burrow are likely to have the body extended when crawling, and to be thickest when burrowing.

Circular muscles are commonly well developed in worms which perform body-wall movements of a peristaltic kind, symmetrical about their own longitudinal axis. Circular muscles are less prominent in *Nereis*, and completely absent in *Nephthys*. In *Nephthys* the longitudinal muscles are antagonized by dorso-ventral muscles, and the hydrostatic pressure is maintained to a large extent by a unique system of ligaments [27, 28]. Longitudinal muscles, on the other hand, attain their greatest development in tube-dwellers where quick end-to-end escape movements are important. In leeches the muscles which spiral round the body may reinforce the circular muscles when the longitudinals are contracted and the body shortened, and the longitudinals when the body is extended.[108]

We have noted that when a living worm is punctured the coelomic fluid usually spurts out, but when anaesthetized the body becomes limp and flaccid. Normally the fluid is kept under a certain pressure by the muscles but the actual pressure maintained varies in different regions of the body of an active worm. Chapman and Newell[22] showed this in the burrowing lugworm, and it is likely that the pressure may be reduced when the worm is completely inactive, and fatigue avoided by the alternation of contraction of different muscles. The hydrostatic pressure of such animals is a measure of their 'strength', or the pressure they can supply to the substratum. Gray and Lissman[70] found experimentally that the maximum pull an earthworm could exert on the substratum was 70 g. This pull was exerted by the worm's longitudinal muscles, which Chapman[22] has calculated as having a cross-sectional area of 0·06 sq cm. Assuming that the strength of a muscle is proportional to its cross-sectional area, the tension produced in the circular muscles of cross-sectional area 0·15 sq cm, should be $\dfrac{70 \times 0·15}{0·06}$ g. Now the pressure exerted on fluid contained in a closed cylinder is expressed by the equation $\dfrac{Tc}{rl}$, where 'Tc' is the total circumferential stress, in this case the tension in the circular muscles, and 'r' and 'l' the radius and length of the cylinder. In the earthworm it follows that the pressure should, therefore, equal $\dfrac{70 \times 0·15}{0·06 \times 0·3 \times 15} = 38$ g/sq cm. The actual pressure measured by Newell,[115] using a water manometer and spoon gauge, was 30 cm, or 30 g/sq cm. Again, Gray and Lissman[70] in their experiments found that the total thrust an earthworm exerts on forward extension is in fact only 2–8 g. According to the calculations of Newell[115] a worm of 0·28 sq cm cross-sectional area with a coelomic pressure of 30 g/sq cm could produce a thrust of 8·5 g, a figure in fair agreement with Gray's and Lissman's measurement. It follows that the forces required for such activities can easily be produced by the contraction of the muscles on the enclosed coelomic fluid.

The bodies of annelids are thus composed of a series of segments bounded at each end by non-segmental regions, enclosing a fluid-filled cavity which is related to the outside by paired coelomoducts and nephridia and through which the gut, blood vessels and nerve cord pass. The repetition of segments imposes an apparent monotony of structure which reflects the muscle-fluid system on which the body works. Much of the morphological variation in annelids does in fact concern structures that do not interfere with this basic arrangement: the prostomium, the parapodia and the gut.

2

FEEDING AND THE STRUCTURE
OF THE GUT

THE gut of annelids like that of other animals is formed
from three parts: a middle region derived from the
endoderm, joined by anterior stomodeal and posterior
proctodeal invaginations of the ectoderm. These divisions
are difficult to recognize in adult annelids, for while it is
generally the ectodermal parts which alone are ciliated in
larvae, cilia may extend throughout the gut in adult worms.
The ability of epithelia of ectodermal origin to secrete a
cuticle is exploited in many worms to line a proboscis or
gizzard. The cuticle of the earthworm gizzard is like that of
the epidermis and is simply collagenous,[63] but in polychaetes
the stomodeal cuticle may be sclerotized to form teeth or
jaws. The stomodeum also gives rise to the anterior end of
the oesophagus, the hinder part being endodermal and
generally less ciliated and more secretory in nature. Nevertheless some enzymes may be secreted in crops derived from
the stomodeum, but most digestion and absorption, whatever the regional specializations might involve, is carried on
in the regions derived from the endoderm. The cells of the
middle region may also secrete a thick chitinous lining.[33]
The posterior ectodermal invagination or proctodeum is
equally difficult to recognize in adult worms, though it too
may remain ciliated.

Apart from being related to the body wall by septa, the
gut is not trammelled by segmentation, and the length of the
different regions has readily been varied according to need.
The order of arrangement of the muscle layers is reversed
as compared with that of the body wall, the inner layer being
circular, the outer longitudinal. The circular layer is well

B*   41

developed in gizzards and some kinds of proboscis. The gizzards of many polychaetes are stomodeal structures and these have unusual muscle cells. The layer of longitudinal muscles is best developed where to-and-fro movements occur. But while the circular layer is often thin, its capacity for peristalsis should not be underestimated.

The intestine is usually as long as the body, but when this is relatively short or stout the middle region of the gut may be coiled, or caeca developed, to provide sufficient digestive surfaces. Many scaleworms and sea-mice have relatively short bodies and the gut is provided with paired caeca. *Sternaspis* is a small, round-bodied burrower in which the septa have mostly broken down and the gut is greatly coiled. Such coiling occurs too in flabelligerids and in some terebellids: all sand- and mud-eaters which may well require a long gut to deal with their food. In all these worms the coiled part of the gut retains its connexion with the body wall only by the dorsal and ventral mesentaries and by septal muscle fibres. Septa are commonly reduced where longitudinal movement of the gut occurs.

The polychaete proboscis

In many polychaetes the stomodeum forms an eversible proboscis. Many oligochaetes also have an eversible or partially eversible proboscis derived from the stomodeum, and so have the rhynchobdellid leeches. As the muscle layers of the gut are reversed in relation to those of the body wall, it is relatively easy for some longitudinal muscles to link the stomodeum with the body wall and to act either as protractors or retractors according to the position of their insertion. Other muscles may be derived from the septa or from the dorsal and ventral mesentaries. Apart from some hesionid polychaetes, the proboscis is not protruded directly as a result of muscular means, however, but indirectly by increased pressure of the coelomic fluid. This may be caused by contraction of the muscles of the body wall, or partly by specialized anterior septa. In most polychaetes, therefore, the largest proboscis muscles are retractors, not protractors. In glycerids the enormous muscles connecting the intestine to the body wall are developed from the dorsal mesentary, and where such development occurs the muscles derived from the mesentaries or septa may alone remain so that movement of coelomic fluid is unimpeded. In lugworms, in the fusiform sand-dwelling opheliids, and in the mud-burrowing *Scalibregma*, the proboscis lies partitioned off by septa which are lacking farther back. The septa may well act as diaphragms maintaining the pressure of the fluid as an integral part of the proboscis mechanism without interfering with the rest of the body.

Other kinds of proboscis have muscles, termed motor muscles, which act both for protraction and retraction. When the proboscis lies retracted within the body, these muscles are directed back on to the proboscis from a forward origin on the body wall, so that on contraction they draw the proboscis forward (protraction). Coelomic fluid pressure may carry the point of insertion on the proboscis past the point of origin on the body wall, which means the muscle is directed forward so that if it then contracts it will act as a retractor. Such muscles do not effect entire retraction and there are other muscles which complete the movement.

In nereids the proboscis forms a muscular mass lying, when retracted, within the first four to twelve segments (fig. 5D). Between this muscular part or 'pharynx' and the mouth is a membranous buccal tube bearing small immovable teeth or paragnaths. This is turned inside out when the proboscis is protruded. The buccal tube is composed of two belts or rings separated by a distinct groove to which muscles arising from the body wall at the hinder edge of the peristomium are inserted. Other muscles attached to the same position are directed back on to the hinder part of the pharynx which contains a single pair of jaws. These may be moved by adductor and abductor muscles arising within the pharynx, which is composed of several layers of differently oriented muscles which enable a variety of crushing movements to be performed. In some species there is a pair of dorso-lateral muscles arising at the hind end of the pharynx and inserted on the body wall. These act as powerful retractors and seem best developed in the most voracious

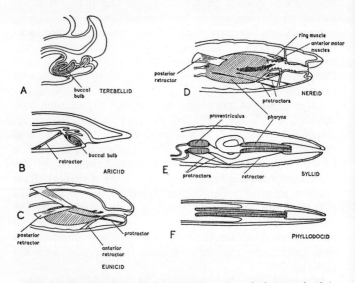

FIG. 5. Modifications of the stomodeum in polychaetes: A, the buccal bulb of terebellids; B, dendritic outgrowths forming the 'secondary' proboscis of ariciids (buccal bulb stippled as in A); C, the ventral proboscis of a eunicid; D, the axial proboscis of a nereid; E, the anterior pharynx and posterior proventriculus of a syllid; F, the simple gizzard-like pharynx of a phyllodocid

species; in mud-eating or algal-eating nereids they are often absent. The two pairs of muscles directed forward from the proboscis to the peristomium act as protractors but they are small. In *Nereis* the buccal tube may be completely turned inside out so as to reveal the jaws, or only partly inverted so that the buccal ring nearest the mouth is alone revealed.

This happens when the worm is digging or when browsing on the surface mud.

A proboscis of a completely different type may be found in the Eunicida, a series of families including a variety of worms some of which are like nereids and others like earth-worms. The proboscis of all these worms is entirely ventral and rather like a shovel in the floor of the mouth (fig. 5C). Its structure is complex, enclosing as it does a series of replaceable teeth and commonly a pair of apposable jaws. Many of these worms are browsers and the paired series of teeth act in them as a kind of radula; others are carnivorous or predatory. In *Marphysa*, for example, a worm which can attain a metre in length, the proboscis extends back as a muscular sac underneath the oesophagus as far as the seventh segment. Within this sac two paired series of jaw-like structures are borne, one dorsal to the other. The larger teeth of the dorsal series (known as 'maxillae') are related by hinges to basal plates which are joined in the mid-line and prolonged backward as a median bar (the 'carrier'). To this bar are related two pairs of muscles directed on to the body wall acting as retractors. The ventral teeth (known as 'mandibles') which lie in the floor of the proboscis, are partly fused together in the mid-line so do not move against one another, though they are moved indirectly by a squeezing action of the whole proboscis. The maxillae are sclerotized parts of the edges of lateral folds of the proboscis cuticle, and the larger ones have abductor and adductor muscles arising from the base of the carrier. In addition to a pair of posterior retractors there is a pair of muscles arising from the body wall in the second segment and inserted on to the base of the ventral mandibles. Another pair of muscles also inserted there arise on the peristomium. These probably account for some degree of eversion, but increased fluid pressure probably plays a part when the proboscis is fully everted.

Arenicola marina has a proboscis quite unlike this. The whole apparatus lies in front of the first septum which almost, but not completely, cuts off an anterior part of the coelom. Fluid pressure within this anterior region is entirely responsible for eversion, while retraction is accomplished by relaxation of the body-wall muscles accompanied by contraction of muscles arising from the junction of the first septum with the body wall and directed forward on to the proboscis. The mechanism and structure of the proboscis in *Arenicola* have been described by Wells[166] in several species which show differences in the details of the mechanism according to habit. A rather similar arrangement is found in *Scalibregma* and in opheliids. All are sand- or mud-eaters, and the loss of septa is no doubt related to the peristaltic movements they make when burrowing.

Sand- and mud-feeders

A great many worms eat sand or mud. Most of them depend on the surface layer, though their burrows are often deep or their tubes long. The nutritional value of sand or mud depends on other organisms or their remains. Level mud deposits in shallow seas often present the densest if not the most varied populations, for within the photic zone the surface layers may support a standing crop of micro-organisms, and may receive a constant rain of organic matter from above. Many worms have adopted methods for gathering the surface deposits while lying in permanent or semi-permanent burrows or tubes. The cirratulids, amphictenids and terebellids have all evolved ciliated, grooved tentacles which search the surface of the mud (figs. 6, 7C, 7E). From such deposit-feeders more specialized suspension-feeders have evolved. *Owenia*, a small cylindrical worm which builds a flexible tube of shell fragments, can feed in both ways. It can collect suspended particles by means of a ciliated crown, and by bending the head over to the surface from the opening of its upright tube can sweep the mud surface.[34]

The muddy sands which *Arenicola marina* and the Californian opheliid *Thoracophelia mucronata* favour have only 1–2% by fresh weight of total organic matter.

But this may not truly represent the amount available, for Krüger[99a] has shown that particles present in the water drawn down the burrow by an irrigating *Arenicola* are caught in the sand in front of the head and are ingested. *Thoracophelia* is a small red worm found in the sandy strands of central California. Like most sand-eaters it seems to be eating continually; McConnaughy and Fox[103] calculated that a worm of 0·04 g (fresh weight) eats about 84 g of sand in a year, and that all the sand in the gut is replaced every 15 minutes. It lives almost at the surface, can rebury itself quickly, and rolls into a tight flat spiral when swept out of the sand by the surf. By allowing itself to be rolled up and down the beach by the waves it keeps within the zone where much organic matter is also left. The gut has a remarkably thin wall, and this is characteristic of other sand-eaters such as *Pectinaria*.

Arenicola marina, when feeding, lies at the bottom of an L-shaped burrow, the head towards the toe of the L, so that the sand caves in to cause a funnel-like depression on the surface. Periodically the worm stops feeding and backs up the vertical shaft of the burrow to defaecate, forming the castings which are such a familiar sight wherever lugworms occur. These activities alternate with some regularity. Wells[165] and Kermack[97] have found that defaecation occurs at intervals of 45 minutes, and that it takes only 15 minutes for sand to reach the rectum after ingestion. The sand is eaten by repeated eversion and retraction of the proboscis, as in opheliids, maldanids, capitellids, *Scalibregma* and the like. Ariciids are also sand- or mud-eaters, but they have a frilly, often dendritic, proboscis with which they lick up the sand much as some holothurians do.

Tentacle-feeders

Deposit-feeding by means of ciliated tentacles has been evolved independently by several groups of polychaetes. The terebellids have particularly extensile tentacles capable of searching a wide area of surface mud. Apart from *Polycirrus* and its allies, which live for the most part under stones and in algal holdfasts, most terebellids have adopted a sedentary life and construct a permanent burrow or tube which they never leave. Many of these worms are quite large, so the ability to glean a wide area for food is important; most are found where the surface has a high organic content which is being constantly replaced. *Lanice conchilega* constructs a frilly top to its tube projecting well above the sand surface on which entangled particles are cleaned off by the tentacles. The top forms a flat fan oriented at right angles to the direction of the current for maximum catch.

The tentacles of terebellids are prostomial in origin and are hollow structures with a complicated musculature enabling them to be moved in a variety of ways (fig. 6). In *Amphitrite johnstoni* the whole of the tentacle surface is provided with mucus cells, and about half is ciliated, the ciliated side being commonly inrolled so as to provide a groove in which the cilia beat towards the mouth. A single narrow longitudinal muscle runs the length of the tentacle at the bottom of the groove, but a much broader longitudinal muscle lines the non-ciliated side. Vertical and transverse muscles link the middle of the ciliated area with the opposite side of the tentacle. There are in addition oblique muscles running in the direction of the axis of the tentacle with their proximal insertions on the side remote from the ciliated groove, and also individual muscle fibres spanning the inner and outer edges of the groove itself. The main longitudinal muscles retract the whole tentacle; the transverse and oblique muscles are for curling and rolling movements, while the individual fibres towards the edges of the groove cause rippling and squeezing movements of the edges (fig. 6F). The tentacles are extended by ciliary creeping, rather like a planarian, the ciliated surface being turned towards the substratum. The tentacle attaches itself by mucus and perhaps also by suction at a point just behind the creeping zone, the coelomic cavity being closed off at this zone of attachment by contraction of the transverse muscles (figs. 6A–D). Coelomic fluid pressure in the whole system is probably equalized by the development of an anterior septum which has sac-like pouches, but the tentacles are not extended by fluid pressure. By the continual release

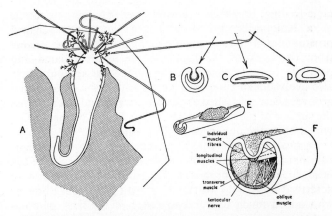

Fig. 6. Feeding and tentacle structure in *Terebella lapidaria*: A, animal in feeding posture beneath a stone; B–D, sections through the extended tentacles: B, showing ciliary gutter, C, tentacle adhering to substratum, D, tentacle turned over and creeping; E, showing sides of gutter gripping particles; F, sterogram to show muscles. Redrawn after Dales[33]

and re-formation of the point of attachment, each tentacle, working independently, gleans from a wide area for food or for debris for the tube. Very small particles are conveyed back along the gutter by ciliary means, but somewhat larger particles are helped by a squeezing action of the sides of the groove. Particles larger still are usually secured by the sides of the groove, and the whole tentacle reeled in. The ciliary groove peters out before the base so that to convey food to the mouth the tentacles are wiped across the lips. It is on these that a certain amount of crude sorting occurs.[33] The lips have a complicated musculature and movement and their development varies with the habit of the species. Broadly speaking, there is an inner pair of lips which form a transverse gutter in the floor of the mouth, preceded by a larger pair derived from the first segment and overhung on the dorsal side by a hood or cowl-shaped upper lip. All these participate in sorting.

Several other groups of polychaetes have adopted tentacle-feeding. *Magelona* is a sand-dweller digging by means of a balloon-like proboscis and a short shovel-shaped prostomium. It has a single pair of long tentacles arising from the back of the head, and these are ciliated and papillate towards their tips (fig. 8D). The spionids have also evolved a single pair of simple tentacles with a ciliated groove. These are lashed about in the water and swept across the surface of the mud, the particles collected by them being wiped on to the underside of the prostomium.[79]

Pectinaria has short feeding tentacles but digs by means of a pair of comb-like rows of chaetae on each side of the head, for it has no proboscis. The habits of *Pectinaria* were described by Arnold Watson,[158] a critical amateur observer who added much to our knowledge of the lives of polychaetes. Various species are noted for the beautifully regular, tall, conical tubes which they build from sand and shell fragments. These tubes are open at both ends, the larger end through which the head can protrude for feeding being directed downwards, the smaller, through which sand may be cast out after passing through the gut, projecting like a chimney just above the surface of the sand. When the worm is feeding the large anterior chaetae form a cage in which the tentacles work (fig. 7D).

Filter-feeders

Some worms which have evolved ciliated tentacles show a tendency towards feeding on particles suspended in the water as well as those on the surface of the mud.

The sabellariids are a group which have partly affected this transition (fig. 7A). Most sabellariids are colonial worms building tubes of sand cemented with mucus. In some parts of the world the tubes are piled together to form massive reefs, the openings of the tubes presenting a honeycomb appearance. Two anterior segments of the worm have become adapted to form an opercular stalk capped by a crown of chaetae which acts as a protective stopper on withdrawal into the tube.[32] On the ventral face of this stalk a mass of feeding tentacles is developed. Each tentacle has a ciliated oral tract, small particles coming in contact adhering and being carried to the mouth. The tentacles are hollow and muscular and capable of a variety of flicking and twisting movements. The particles they catch travel in well-defined ciliary tracts towards the mouth where some selection occurs.

Of true filter-feeders we know most about the feeding habits of *Chaetopterus* from the studies of McGinitie,[104] and of sabellids from E. A. T. Nicol.[116] *Chaetopterus* (fig. 8C) strains the water it pumps through the tube; sabellids strain water passed through a ciliated crown expanded beyond the tube opening.

In *Chaetopterus* the current is produced by three pairs of notopodia each fused in the mid-line with its partner on the other side, and each scooping out the water from in front and expanding to fill the lumen of the tube as it does so. This is no mere to-and-fro motion; their movements are complex and beautifully co-ordinated. Some distance in front of these pumping parapodia another pair of notopodia are arched over the back, their tips touching to form a ring. Into this ring mucus is secreted and this is drawn out to form a membrane dragged back by the stream of water to form a thimble-shaped bag in which suspended matter is caught. This is one of the most efficient filters devised by animals, particles as small as 40 Å being retained. McGinitie found that as the bag became loaded it was carried down into a cup-shaped structure where it was rolled into a ball and passed forward along a ciliary groove to the mouth. Wells found in one instance that about 290 ml was pumped through each bag which was renewed every 20 minutes.[167]

In the sabellid and serpulid fanworms the filter is provided by branched or pinnate prostomial 'tentacles' which are held stiffly out to form a feathery crown through which the water is strained (fig. 7B). The main filaments or rays of the crown are spread open by the springy skeletal rods which support them. On the upper or oral side of both the main filaments and the pinnules there are short cilia which beat towards the mouth. On their lateral edges are longer cilia which draw water from the outside of the crown to the centre. Particles in the water tend to fall on to the upper, oral, or frontal surfaces of the filaments as they eddy between them, and those coming in contact with any part adhere, if small enough, and are conveyed by mucus driven by cilia towards the base. Here each ciliary tract meets another leading to the mouth. The crown is a bilateral structure being formed of two parts separated mid-dorsally, so that the tract leading to the mouth is in the form of a split-ring. In *Sabella pavonina* mechanical sorting of particles occurs on the filaments, especially towards the base where the particles are guided into a gutter-like gauge.[116] Only the smallest particles falling to the bottom of this gutter reach the mouth. Large particles tend to ride up the sides of the gauge and are collected by a counter-current along the edges of the gutter and along the collar-like flaps overlapping the tracts leading to the mouth, and are then rejected along a pair of specialized filaments in the centre of the crown. Here the rejected particles are caught in the ascending and rapidly moving current which has already passed through the filaments. Incidentally, it is into this stream that faecal pellets are also ejected, a ciliary groove on the body wall curling round on to the dorsal side to terminate in the mid-dorsal notch of the crown. Particles of intermediate size reaching the sorting gutter at the base of a filament may be rejected or incorporated into the tube. The ciliary currents over the base of the crown are quite complicated.

The filtering mechanism is much the same in other sabellids and serpulids. In *Sabella spallanzanii* (often known as *Spirographis*) the halves of the crown are spiralled, one side being larger than the other; in *Bispira* they are roughly equal as the name implies; in *Schizobranchia* the filaments are branched; but all cause a current to sweep up through the back of the crown to the centre. The filaments are joined towards the base by a thin membrane, and in *Myxicola* this membrane is extended towards the tips of the filaments so that water can only enter near the rim of the crown. This may be related to the fact that the crown is opened flush with the surface of the mud in which their tubes are buried. At the base of the crown in sabellids there is a mid-ventral notch in the collar revealing the special glands and lip-like folds concerned with tube building. The collar in serpulids is continuous mid-ventrally, for these worms secrete a limy tube and in them the ciliary tracts and sorting mechanisms are simpler. By measuring the decrease in optical density of colloidal carbon suspensions in which sabellids and serpulids feed normally, it has been found that smaller worms filter at relatively higher rates than larger ones, as might be expected: *Pomatoceros* weighing about 0·018 g filters about 27 ml/hr; *Myxicola* weighing about 2·7 g filters 290 ml/hr. Particles as small as 1–2μ can be caught, but a large proportion of micro-organisms escape.[35] Some micro-organisms are distasteful but others of similar size are retained: *Sabella pavonina* and *S. spallanzanii* dislike *Phaeodactylum tricornutum*, but will remove *Dunaliella* or *Isochrysis* from suspension quite as readily as colloidal carbon particles of similar size.

The development of a filtering crown for feeding has made the sabellids and serpulids the most elegant of all the annelids. But they are not the only ones that have adopted suspension-feeding. *Owenia* has developed, independently, a small crown with which it can trap particles in suspension.[34] The crown is small by comparison with those of sabellids and serpulids, and takes the form of a shallow bowl with a frilly, dichotomously branching edge. These branches are provided with cilia which eddy particles into the crown and direct them from the edges into a gutter leading to the mouth. Particles may be rejected by flicking movements of individual branches or by convulsive movements of the whole crown, which as a consequence has a complex musculature.

The gut in polychaetes

The morphology of the gut in polychaetes is more variable than might at first appear.

In *Arenicola* the oesophagus leads from the stomodeum to a yellowish stomach and intestine together lying in the trunk or aseptate part of the body, and thence to a rectum in the tail. The oesophagus is divisible histologically into two regions behind the most anterior part which lies in front of the first septum, and which being lined with cuticle is probably of stomodeal origin. The stomach also has two regions.[97] The part of the oesophagus passing through the anterior septa has a thick muscular coat with a simple epithelial lining forming papillae arranged in roughly longitudinal rows. Here there are no cilia. Immediately behind the most posterior of these septa the oesophagus is more glandular, the muscle layer thinner, and the epithelium partly ciliated. From this region a pair of oesophageal pouches arise. These pouches, though thin-walled, are capable of muscular contraction and are lined by a simple squamous epithelium. The anterior part of the stomach into which the oesophagus opens has a much wider lumen, is thin-walled, and has a poor musculature. It is lined with a simple epithelium, some cells apparently being phagocytic, others ciliated. Ciliated cells increase in number and converge posteriorly in the hind stomach to form a ventral ciliated gutter which continues to the anus. The hind stomach has a more infolded wall and there are mucus and enzyme-secreting cells. From this there is a gradual transition to the intestine which has a narrower lumen; the rectum is bound by the septa to the body wall of the tail, but though thin-walled is capable of distension. Kermack[97] found considerable water absorption in the 'trunk gut' with a weakly acid pH (5·4–6·0) in the stomach. This she found to be the main region of digestion. Kermack also found that food particles in the stomach were taken up phagocytically by certain epithelial cells which passed on their particles to the amoebocytes at the base; these moved either into the blood-stream or into the peritoneum. While sand takes only 15 minutes to pass through the trunk gut, the rectum is distended until full, defaecation occurring at intervals of about 45 minutes. A high rate of eating may be necessary where the food consists of only 1–2% organic matter, and phagocytic activity may be important in cutting down the amount of enzyme required to be released into such a relatively high proportion of indigestible matter.

How far does the gut of other sand-eaters resemble that of *Arenicola*? Actually we know few others in detail; McConnaughy and Fox[103] have studied *Thoracophelia*, Ullman and Bookhout[155] *Clymenella*, Brasil[17] *Pectinaria*. *Thoracophelia* is a worm commonly only 3–4 cm in length. It has a narrow oesophagus leading to a wider stomach, in turn leading to a somewhat narrower intestine and a short rectum. The stomach is much involuted when empty, especially on its ventral side, thereby considerably increasing its surface area, while the intestine has a mid-ventral ciliated tract leading into the rectum which probably functions for respiration. In *Clymenella torquata* the long ciliated oesophagus, which has gland cells posteriorly, passes into an unciliated stomach which probably serves mainly for storage. This leads abruptly to an intestine divisible histologically into four regions. The first two regions have secretory cells, but the first has tall columnar cells with short cilia; the second contains a greater variety of secretory cells with a brush border and may be partly absorptive. The third region may be entirely absorptive while the fourth seems to have large numbers of mucus-secreting cells. The whole intestine has convoluted walls increasing its surface area and is distinguished from the stomach by the ventral ciliated groove. *Pectinaria* has a thin-walled looped gut twice the length of the body. In all these worms the gut tends to be delicate, distensible and long, the ciliated oesophagus passing to a non-ciliated secretory region followed by an absorptive region with a ciliated ventral groove passing through the storing rectum.

Amongst more specialized deposit-feeders such as the terebellids *Amphitrite johnstoni* and *Terebella lapidaria*, Dales[33] and Sutton[150] have found that the long ciliated oesophagus is posteriorly glandular and opens into a large anterior stomach provided with secretory cells with a brush border. This leads into a hind stomach with a very muscular wall with a chitinous lining and acting as a mixer. There is a similar development in sabellariids. A long intestine which is apparently absorptive leads imperceptibly from this into a terminal rectum. In *Amphitrite johnstoni* the intestine is coiled anteriorly within a short aseptate region, greatly increasing the absorptive length; as before, a ventral ciliated groove starts at the junction of the hind stomach with the intestine and continues to the anus. The hind intestine is ciliated and mucus cells increase in number posteriorly just as in *Clymenella*; they presumably bind the faeces. In *Amphitrite johnstoni* the pH of the fore stomach is about 6·0 in a feeding worm, and the contents become progressively more alkaline farther back. In *Terebella lapidaria* there is some evidence that absorption takes place in the fore stomach as well as in the intestine.[150]

The rectum, where the faeces accumulate, is particularly long in worms which for one reason or another defaecate at long intervals. In *Owenia* it is almost as long as the intestine, which, like the anterior stomach, has cells with a brush border. In *Owenia* the gut is externally simple and straight, but the regions are abruptly marked histologically. The short, ciliated and mucus-producing oesophagus leads to a relatively thin-walled stomach with cells which are presumably enzyme-secreting. The intestine into which it passes is apparently absorptive.[34] It is this region that has a deep green colour, just as that of *Chaetopterus* has, and for the same reason, for in both the colour is due to phaeophorbides—breakdown products of chlorophylls presumably derived from the food.[34, 96]

In all deposit-feeders examined there is a more or less localized secretory stomach leading to a predominantly absorptive intestine in which a ventral ciliated groove is to be found, as in less-selective sand-eaters. The muscular coat is thin except for regions such as the gizzard or hind stomach in terebellids and sabellariids, but it should be realized that even a thin coat is capable of peristalsis. The direction of such squeezing movements is frequently towards the mouth, not the anus; indeed in *Sabella* antiperistalsis seems to be the rule, and it has been suggested that this may assist mixing of the contents. A great deal of the transmission of the gut contents, however, is undoubtedly affected indirectly by a squeezing action of the body wall. The ciliary groove in the intestine may help to remove indigestible matter from the site of absorption; its cilia beat towards the anus.

In true suspension-feeders such as sabellids and serpulids the gut may be entirely ciliated from one end to the other, so that there is no differentiation of an intestinal ciliary gutter. In the gut of *Sabella pavonina* we may distinguish only four regions: the oesophagus, stomach (manifestly secretory), intestine (clearly absorptive) and rectum in which there are numerous mucus cells.[116] The same regions may be distinguished in the serpulid *Pomatoceros*.

Of the structure of the gut of polychaetes that have become carnivorous we know much less, though the gut of the carnivorous scaleworms, for example, certainly differs widely from those of the worms just considered. In scaleworms the oesophagus leads to an 'intestine' into which project irregular papillae or folds composed of groups of tall cells. Some of these are secretory and no doubt digestive. From the intestine paired caeca arise in which both digestion and absorption take place. Fordham[56] found in *Aphrodite aculeata* that the neck of each caecum was guarded by cells on each side, forming an effective sieve chamber which allowed only very small particles of food to enter the caecum. The caecum has a complex epithelium in which several kinds of secretory and absorptive cell may be distinguished. Darboux[42] found some evidence that materials injected into the coelom were finally excreted into them by special cells. But the caeca deserve further study, for some of the cells contain a brownish substance which can be ejected through the anus—it has been suggested, in defence. The rectum is also rather different from other worms in having a series of strongly ciliated ridges projecting into it.

Feeding and gut structure in oligochaetes

On turning to the Oligochaeta we find that many of the smallest worms are also active predators, though some live on detritus, and the earthworms live mostly on organic remains in the soil. In earthworms the mouth is usually described as opening into a short buccal cavity leading into a pharynx which is dilatable and globular in shape. The cavity of the pharynx may be enlarged by contraction of muscles radiating from it to the body wall so that soil is sucked up. The pharynx is also protrusile, at least in *Lumbricus terrestris*, though this has been observed in relation to burrowing rather than feeding. Earthworms profoundly modify the soil structure by constantly passing it through their bodies and casting it to the surface. Darwin wrote a book about this.

The sucking action of the pharynx has also been utilized by some smaller but often rapaceous aquatic oligochaetes. *Agriodrilus vermivorus* of Lake Baikal, for example, lives on other small worms which it catches in this way; *Chaetogaster diaphanus* has similar habits, feeding on small invertebrates such as bottom-living Cladocera. Others, such as *Aulophorus*, have developed a different mechanism. Marcus[109] has described a dorsal glandular subdivision of the pharynx to which muscles are attached enabling it to be protruded as a pad-like tongue. The gland cells, which in some other polychaetes form distinct 'salivary' glands, produce mucus and also, apparently, a protease. The pharyngeal glands of earthworms are also mainly mucus-producers, the mucus lubricating the food, and while often stated to contain a protease, van Gansen[62] has found no evidence for this in *Eisenia foetida*.

In the aquatic oligochaetes the oesophagus is generally ciliated, but this is not so in earthworms. In them there are specialized outpushings known as the calciferous glands which often have a complicated detailed structure, and in which the epithelium is thrown into radially arranged lamellae. They have been the subject of some attention, and the general conclusion seems to be that they act as regulators in getting rid of excess calcium.[112, 133] Calcium is secreted into the gut in the form of calcite but this has no neutralizing effect on the gut contents as was once thought. Bevelander and Nakahara[11] have found their activity to be cyclical. Robertson showed that about 10% of the metabolic carbon dioxide of the body was eliminated in this way, and Dotterweich and Franke that the calciferous glands also regulate magnesium, strontium and phosphate.

In earthworms ingested soil is led from the oesophagus through a crop and gizzard to the intestine in which both secretory and absorptive cells are found. Van Gansen[63] has shown that in *Eisenia foetida* proteases are also secreted in the crop. The surface of the intestine is increased by a dorsal longitudinal involution known as the typhlosole. This is large in lumbricids, but small in some other earthworms such as megascolecids and glossoscolecids. In some megascolecids and a few enchytraeids there are additional glands opening into the intestine. As in polychaetes the pH in the earthworm intestine does not vary very much from neutrality.

It has been mentioned that some movement of the gut contents is due to an indirect action of the body wall, but all parts of the gut, however thinly muscled, are capable of constricting movements which may travel in either direction. Pieces of excised gut from both oligochaetes and polychaetes undergo rhythmic contractions. Wu[175] suspected that the earthworm gut was innervated by antagonistic nerves which were adrenergic and cholinergic respectively. Millott[111] showed that this was indeed the case in *Lumbricus terrestris*. It had been known for some time that the gut receives a nervous supply from the oesophageal ring, but Millott demonstrated that this was supplemented by a dual system of nerves entering the gut in each segment across the septa from the body wall. This system of nerves, controlling the tonus of the gut behind the oesophagus, is composed of cholinergic augmentors fired from the median and posterior segmental nerves through the body wall and entering the gut ventro-laterally across each septum, and adrenergic inhibitors also fired through the anterior segmental nerves and entering dorso-laterally. Physiologically the whole control of tonus recalls the sympathetic and parasympathetic system of vertebrates. We have no knowledge of whether there is a similar mechanism in other annelids, but it is clear that the movements of the gut are delicately controlled, and that the contents are mixed and moved in a variety of ways.

The gut and feeding of leeches

There remain to be considered the feeding habits and structure of the gut in leeches, and those of other annelids which have become parasitic.

The rhynchobdellid leeches have evolved an eversible proboscis, but the most familiar leeches are gnathobdellids or pharyngobdellids which have a muscular pharynx which is not eversible. The gnathobdellids have apposable teeth formed from the sclerotized cuticle of the buccal cavity and provided with powerful muscles. The rhynchobdellid proboscis is derived from the muscular pharynx, and has acquired some protrusive ability by virtue of an epidermal involution round the mouth. Its action, like those of all oligochaetes and leeches, is sucking. Leeches have one or more pairs of 'salivary' glands producing an anti-coagulant, 'hirudin', preventing the blood from clotting as it is ingested. Leggenhager thought that hirudin from the medicinal leech, *Hirudo*, acted by inhibiting thrombokinase. On the other hand, Lindemann maintained that the actual flow of blood from the wound was aided by a histamine-like compound which dilated the capillaries.[108] Most leeches can take a vast meal when occasion permits. *Hirudo* can gorge itself to six or ten times its initial weight at a single meal, and this ability was made great use of by the medical profession in the days when blood-letting was fashionable. The ability to gorge in this way is made possible by the oesophagus opening into a 'stomach' from which paired and greatly distensible caeca arise. The stomach opens through a sphincter into an intestine in turn leading to a short ciliated rectum. The stomach has a varied epithelial structure with both secretory and absorptive cells. It is the globin of the ingested blood which is mainly utilized as food by the leech. Some leeches have caeca for bacteria opening off the oesophagus; Reichenow described these in *Placobdella*, and they have since been found in other glossiphoniids. In these leeches the bacteria are apparently inside the cells, but in *Piscicola* they occur in the lumen. Büsing and his colleagues[21] discovered that *Hirudo* depends entirely on the gut bacteria, in this instance *Pseudomonas hirudinis*, for digestion, and it would seem that the gut wall itself has lost the ability to produce at least the proteolytic enzymes. *Haemopis* has not gone quite as far as this, but is still apparently largely dependent on the bacteria in its gut.

Parasites

Most leeches are specialized predators, but some piscicolids are more parasitic in habit in that they remain with a specific host: *Calliobdella lophii* is found on angler fish; *Hemibdella soleae* on soles; *Ostreobdella* on oysters.

Few polychaetes are parasites and most of these show little or no obvious morphological modification for this way of life. One exception is *Histriobdella*. This highly specialized eunicidan has only a single pair of parapodia at the hind end of the body, and with these it walks with ridiculous assurance over the gills or eggs of lobsters in berry. *Oligognathus*, another parasitic eunicidan, may attain a length of 10 cm within the coelom of the echiuroid,

Bonellia, but perhaps the most curious is *Haematocleptes terebellides* found inside the dorsal blood vessel of the terebellid *Terebellides stroemi* by Wiren. There are many other eunicidans, mostly arabellids, found inside the bodies of other worms. Nothing is known of how they get there. The most famous ectoparasitic polychaete is probably *Ichthyotomus* which was found on the gills of the eel *Myra* at Naples. These tiny worms grow no longer than 1 cm, and attain sexual maturity on reaching 2 mm. They attach themselves by a pair of scissor-like jaws which open on relaxation so as to lock into the host's tissues. The jaws move on each other by a ball-and-socket action, and protrude from a dimpled inpushing round the mouth forming a minute sucker. Another ectoparasitic polychaete is *Calamyzas amphictenicola,* a little syllid from the ampharetid *Amphicteis.* Sense organs and many other external features are much reduced, the females having the posterior segments enlarged by the gonads.

The myzostomids, undoubtedly of polychaete derivation as indicated by their larval life, morphology and chaetae, are considered by Jägersten[88] as a distinct class. All are parasites on or in echinoderms, mostly crinoids, including our own *Antedon.* A few are found in brittle-stars, and the Mediterranean starfish *Asterias richardi* and *Stolasterias neglecta* suffer them as internal parasites. Most myzostomids when mature are small flattened discs, almost without internal segmentation, but externally with a series of reduced parapodia and hook-shaped chaetae. The young at first walk about—looking rather like tardigrades—before finding a host. Most of them are protandrous hermaphrodites. *Protomyzostomum* is found in the brittle-star *Gorgonocephalus* in which it feeds on the gonads.

Perhaps even fewer oligochaetes than polychaetes are known to have adopted a parasitic life, but those that have show interesting structural modifications. The enchytraeid, *Aspidodrilus kelsalli,* is found in the branchial chambers of crayfishes; it looks like a minute leech, the body being short and the posterior segments modified as a kind of adhesive pad with a small anterior sucker. *Pelmatodrilus planariformis* is found on certain earthworms in Jamaica. It is a somewhat flattened worm and has the ventral surface covered with minute chaetae with which it can cling to and move over the surface of its host. Michaelsen even found an oligochaete within the Wolffian ducts of certain tree frogs in South America. The modifications of the gut in such aberrant worms are unknown and await investigation.

3

THE EVOLUTION OF POLYCHAETES

IN CONSIDERING the evolution of the Polychaeta we are
faced with two difficulties. First, the existing families are
very distinct, an aspect perhaps of their antiquity, and
secondly, there are no fossils worth mentioning. It should
also be realized that the division into Errantia and Sedentaria found in most books is not a natural one.

The ancestral annelids from which the polychaetes are
derived were probably small creatures living in offshore
deposits. The body was segmented and septate in adaptation
to burrowing and crawling, chaetae had developed to grip
the substratum, and they fed on detritus and micro-
organisms in which such surface deposits are rich. A ciliated
mucus-producing stomodeum with a partially protrusile
muscular 'tongue' in the floor of the buccal cavity probably
developed early in their evolution, for such a structure is
retained today in the heterogeneous assemblage of genera
known as the Archiannelida.

With increasing size various other ways of collecting food
from the mud surface were evolved, and many worms
developed ciliated tentacles of various kinds from the
prostomium for this purpose. This line of evolution led to
tentacle-feeders such as the ampharetids and terebellids;
and from worms collecting particles on the surface the
sabellid and serpulid fanworms were evolved which filtered
particles suspended in the water. In others a burrowing habit
was adopted with the evolution of an eversible proboscis
capable of both digging through the mud and also ingesting
it; worms represented today by the lugworms, capitellids and
Ophelia. Another line of evolution led to feeding on larger
particles, to scavenging, algal-eating and predation. In these

64

polychaetes a more elaborate eversible proboscis is found, with a muscular gizzard-like pharynx often armed with teeth. The clue, in fact, to the evolution of the Polychaeta seems to lie in the structures formed from the stomodeum.[40]

The Archiannelida are a heterogeneous assemblage of genera of which *Polygordius, Protodrilus, Saccocirrus, Nerilla* and *Dinophilus* are the best known. None of these is closely related to any of the others, and each shows different specializations. Most are small, active creatures of scavenging habit, with a protrusile tongue-like buccal bulb. This consists of a muscular pad in the floor of the buccal cavity formed from myoepithelial cells and joined to the body wall by extrinsic muscles, all of which are derived from the ectoderm of the stomodeum. *Polygordius* seems the most distinct genus, with a specialized larval development quite unlike that of other archiannelids. Jägersten found that it alone amongst the other genera lacked a buccal bulb.[40] Archiannelids are found scuttling in surface silt, in sand or in the splash pools near high-water mark. *Protodrilus* and *Saccocirrus* have long tentacles on the head; *Nerilla* is reminiscent of syllids, and *Dinophilus* might be mistaken for a eunicid larva were it not for the absence of jaws. It has been suggested that all archiannelids are specialized members of other families, but it seems better to regard these genera as remnants of early annelid stock each of which has become specialized in different ways.

From the ancestral stock of which the archiannelids of today are specialized survivals, several independent lines of evolution diverged in the remote past leading to the families of polychaetes we know now. A ventral buccal organ similar to the buccal bulb of archiannelids is retained in pectinariids (amphictenids), ampharetids and terebellids (fig. 5A), related families that have evolved feeding tentacles which are extended into or on to the surface of the mud or sand in which they live. This buccal organ is used as a lip and food sorter as described in the preceding chapter. Most of these worms live in permanent burrows or tubes. These are built from materials gathered by the tentacles and

C

lips and bound with mucus secreted from special ventral glands. The ampharetids (fig. 7E) and terebellids (fig. 6) are clearly related, although the ampharetids differ from terebellids in their ability to withdraw their tentacles within the stomodeum. The pectinariids (fig. 7D) probably diverged from the same stock at an earlier period; they also have a mass of ciliated feeding tentacles of prostomial origin, and have developed the large anterior chaetae, seen also in ampharetids, into digging combs. Some pectinariids are sand- rather than mud-dwellers, and all are noted for the beauty of the conical tubes they build to protect their delicate bodies. Members of all three families tend to be plump, with short parapodia often reduced to mere ridges. Gills are developed behind the head near the tube opening, and septa are often reduced; all of these are adaptations to a life in a permanent burrow or tube.

The cirratulids may possibly be derived from related but probably not the same stock. The curious little stygo- capitellids may also be an early offshoot. Cirratulids (fig. 7C) are mostly mud-dwellers, feeding by means of tentacles, not however of prostomial origin, and by a ventral prehensile tongue reminiscent of the archiannelid buccal bulb. Most cirratulids are cylindrical worms with poorly developed parapodia, and long respiratory cirri emerging dorso-laterally from many of the segments. These cirri are thrust up through the mud to lie on the surface very like the feeding tentacles. In the cirratulids the tendency towards tentacle-feeding culminates in *Dodecaceria*, some species of which form massive limy reefs.

The ariciids also have a buccal organ when they are larvae, but this is functionally replaced in the adult by secondary, frilly, often dendritic, processes from the walls of the eversible stomodeum (fig. 5B). Most ariciids live in mud or sand, and like many other burrowers they have a simple conical prostomium devoid of appendages, though most have well-developed notopodial gills and frilly neuropodia farther back.

Owenia also has a buccal organ,[171] here used for ingestion

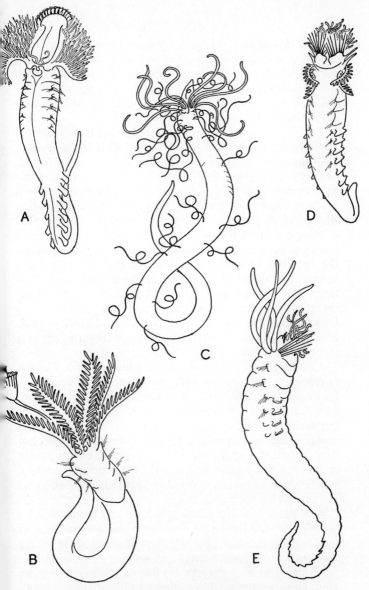

FIG. 7. Some tentacle-bearing polychaetes: A, a sabellariid;
B, a serpulid; C, a cirratulid; D, a pectinariid; E, an ampharetid
(not drawn to the same scale)

and tube building. *Owenia*, as already noted, feeds by means of a ciliated crown developed from the prostomium; its relative, *Myriochele*, has a simpler ciliated funnel. Both are cylindrical worms with elongate segments rather like maldanids, without projections and adapted to the close-fitting but flexible tubes which they build.

The development of ciliated feeding structures from the prostomium is taken further in the sabellids and serpulids; they show no vestige of a buccal organ, even in the larvae. We can only guess that the sabellids arose from some ampharetid-like deposit-feeding ancestor that had developed grooved ciliated tentacles from the prostomium. The trailing of these in the water with the development of marginal cilia, causing a current to pass between them, could have given rise to a more efficient strainer by the development within the tentacles of a simple supporting skeleton to form a crown. The sabellids build tubes from sand and shell fragments rejected from the feeding currents, and bind them with mucus. Serpulids, on the other hand, secrete limy tubes, a process studied by Swan[151] and Hedley,[78] and have modified one of the filaments of the crown to act as a stopper to the tube on retraction.

Another family of polychaetes in which no buccal organ is recognizable is the Flabelligeridae (or Chloraemidae as they used to be called). These specialized mud-dwellers share with the ampharetids the development of prostomial feeding tentacles, but are quite different in having the most anterior segments inversive. Their affinities are obscure, but they possess the green respiratory pigment chlorocruorin in the blood, a feature shared only with the ampharetids, sabellids and serpulids. It could be that they are all derived from the same ancestor.

A completely independent group is the Psammodrilidae described by Swedmark.[152] These are small worms living in sand with a peculiar pharyngeal mechanism quite unlike that of any other polychaete.

All the remaining polychaetes have a proboscis of some kind. Of these, three groups appear to be different from all the others in having a proboscis which is entirely ventral: the amphinomids, the eunicids and their allies, and the spionid-like worm, *Magelona*. We cannot say that these ventral structures are elaborations of buccal organs, though this may be their origin, but it does appear that each of these groups is phylogenetically isolated and shows no real affinity with any family in which an axial or symmetrical proboscis is found.

The amphinomids are curious animals with several peculiarities isolating them from other families. They have calcareous chaetae which easily break off, the points remaining in the skin and causing irritation; they are worms to be handled with caution! Amphinomids are characteristic of warmer seas, some having short, bristly bodies like some aphroditid sea-mice. Others are elongate. All of them have a lobe projecting back from the prostomium known as the caruncle and four longitudinal nerve cords. They browse on sedentary animals such as sponges and hydroids, the ventral proboscis forming a horny rasp. The most specialized of them, often separated as a distinct family, the Spintheridae, are more or less parasitic on sponges, and are flattened disc-shaped creatures with the same colour as the sponge on which they feed.

The Eunicida comprise a group of families united by having a ventral proboscis of essentially similar structure with a rather characteristic armature of replaceable teeth and jaws (fig. 5C). The Eunicida have undergone an adaptive radiation into algal-eaters, voracious predators, and tube-dwellers, ancient enough for some lines (such as the arabellids and lumbrinereids) to have converged. Prostomial tentacles and notopodial gills, which are often elaborately branched or comb-like structures arched over the back, are often well developed in those which live in tubes or burrows. The quill-worm *Hyalinoecia*, belongs here; it crawls about on the surface by means of the anterior parapodia, the rest of the body being protected by a transparent horny tube into which the worm can completely retract. Others are more like earthworms, completely devoid of appendages.

Magelona, in spite of its superficial resemblance to spionids, has many structural peculiarities which isolate it. All species are small elongate worms living in sandy beaches, with pointed trowel-like prostomiums and a single pair of long papillate tentacles with which they feed. Amongst other peculiar features they have enucleate corpuscles containing the respiratory pigment haemerythrin, unique in the Annelida, and found elsewhere only in the sipunculids. The proboscis of *Magelona* is a simple balloon-like structure forming a sac ventral to the oesophagus when retracted.

On turning to those families in which the proboscis is an axial, symmetrical organ, we find that there are two main series of families, one of which may be further subdivided. The first of these includes worms like *Arenicola* and *Ophelia* in which the proboscis is a relatively simple eversible buccal tube. The second includes *Nereis* and *Aphrodite* in which the eversible buccal tube leads to a muscular gizzard-like pharynx.

The worms which have a simple, relatively thin-walled proboscis are all sand- or mud-eaters; the proboscis is thrown out as a result of fluid pressure, and it is often partly isolated in an anterior coelom cut off by septa from the most anterior of which, in *Arenicola* at least, retractor muscles are derived. In opheliids, *Scalibregma* and maldanids the proboscis is very much alike in these respects. To these we may also add the capitellids, which, although having the most anterior septum situated farther back, have retractor muscles in front of it which may well be derived from septal muscles. The arenicolids, *Scalibregma*, and many opheliids, are stout worms with simple prostomiums and short notopodial gills, arborescent in *Arenicola* and *Scalibregma*, simple and slender in opheliids. The maldanids have simple cylindrical bodies, the head often flat, obliquely truncated and oval, and the pygidium expanded into a funnel round the anus.

The proboscis of *Sternaspis* is also simple, and it may be that this specialized annelid has diverged from the same stock of the arenicolids and opheliids. Certainly its apparent resemblances to the echiuroids are due to convergence. *Sternaspis* (fig. 8B) is a grey, rounded worm, commonly the size of a large pea, with a broad sclerotized plate at its posterior end round which numerous serpentine gills protrude. The worm lies just under the surface of the mud, head down, with the gills on the surface.

Of the spionids, genera such as *Scolelepis* also have a simple proboscis used for digging, though this tends to be lost in the more specialized borers such as *Polydora*. A simple proboscis is found, too, in the paraonids, disomids and in *Poecilochaetus*, which are related to them. Most of these worms are small, with a single pair of anterior feeding tentacles, and live in burrows, sandy tubes, or bore into limestone or shells such as those of oysters. In the spionid line of evolution we may see a transition from sand-eating by means of a proboscis to tentacle-feeding with consequent proboscis loss. The tentacles arise in the larva in a dorso-lateral position behind the head, and, unlike those of ampharetids, terebellids and flabelligerids, these are innervated by nerves arising at the back of the brain behind those received from the nuchal organs. Similar, and similarly innervated, tentacles are found in the Sabellariidae, a family in which there is no vestige of either a buccal organ or proboscis, and which feed, it may be remembered, by means of a secondary tentacle system. The two larval tentacles remain the main feeding structures in primitive sabellariids such as *Phalacrostemma*, but these are progressively reduced in more advanced genera with the growth of the secondary tentacles.

While the sabellariids have exploited the tentacle method of feeding initiated by their spioniform forbears, the chaetopterids have tended to abandon the tentacles in favour of improving the current passed through the tube for respiratory reasons, and straining it through mucus for food. In the primitive *Phyllochaetopterus* and *Ranzania* the current is still ciliary, as in spionids, and it is only in *Chaetopterus* that muscular pumping, which greatly increases the rate of flow through the tube, is adopted. *Chaetopterus* is completely dependent on these strainings for food, but the spioniform tentacles are still recognizable and assist the food into the mouth (fig. 8C). The more primitive chaetopterids are very like spionids with their long anterior tentacles, but like *Chaetopterus* all of them live permanently in tough, horny tubes, often of great length, and have cups and ciliated tracts along the back. *Chaetopterus* itself has perhaps the most highly differentiated series of segments of any polychaete.

The spionids, chaetopterids and sabellariids may be grouped together as an order, the Spionida. The arenicolids, opheliids and so on may be grouped into another order, the Capitellida. In these two groups of families, then, we may recognize the transition from ingestion of mud and sand by means of a simple proboscis to worms in which this is relegated entirely to a digging function with assumption of feeding tentacles. This change is followed by loss of the proboscis with the development of tube building or boring. The tentacles themselves are in turn replaced by a more elaborate tentacle system in the sabellariids, and by filter-feeding by means of a mucus-bag in chaetopterids.

All the worms belonging to the remaining families of polychaetes have a muscular pharynx and are predatory or scavenging in habit. There are three groups of families of which the phyllodocids are perhaps the most generalized. The Phyllodocidae, so called from the leaf-like notopodia, are mostly small, actively crawling worms with a long series of similar segments. From them the pelagic alciopids have been derived, differing most noticeably in their relatively enormous eyes. The fusiform typhloscolecids, also found only in oceanic plankton, are of more uncertain affinity; they were possibly derived neotenously from phyllodocid stock. The pelagic tomopterids, notable for the complete loss of chaetae apart from the large anterior acicula, have the parapodia adapted as paddles. They are also of very doubtful affinity. In the phyllodocids and alciopids the proboscis is generally long and the muscular pharynx tubular (fig. 5F).

The Nephthyidae, the Glyceridae and their derivatives the

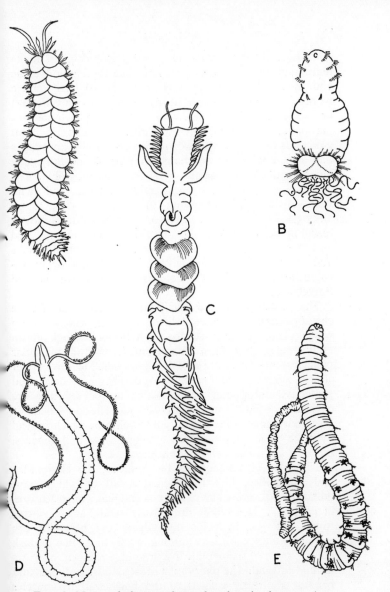

Fig. 8. More polychaetes often referred to in the text: A, a polynoid; B, *Sternaspis*; C, *Chaetopterus*; D, *Magelona*; E, *Arenicola marina* (not drawn to the same scale)

goniadids, the Sphaerodoridae and Pisionidae, all make temporary burrows in the sand, but like the Phyllodocidae and their pelagic descendants they are all fairly active worms. The nephthyids are strong swimmers with yellowish or pearly muscular bodies, with well-developed foliaceous parapodia and small prostomiums. The glycerids and goniadids are cylindrical worms, with reduced appendages and long, conical prostomiums. They are like nephthyids in having little body pigment apart from haemoglobin. The glycerids and nephthyids are rapid burrowers and swim well. Little is known about the sphaerodorids, found amongst algal holdfasts. Pisionids are small worms mostly found in sandy beaches; they have the prostomium reduced and merged with anterior segments. Like the phyllodocids and their allies they all have protonephridia or proto-nephromixia which are not found elsewhere in the Polychaeta.

The scaleworms, and the relatively rare and fragile chrysopetalids related to them, form a second group which probably diverged from phyllodocid stock at an early stage; they have mixonephridia and a muscular pharynx reminiscent of those of nephthyids. Most live under stones, in crevices and some in sand. They have developed protective notopodial scales, which in the sea-mice are overlaid by a felt of long, slender chaetae. The chrysopetalids owe their name to the broad, golden chaetae which project over the back; they scavenge amongst algae and crevices, but they are minute and seldom seen.

The third group includes the Syllidae, the Hesionidae and Pilargiidae, and the Nereidae, all of which have metanephridia or metanephromixia and many other features in common. The syllids are mostly small, active worms found amongst hydroids and algae; the hesionids are extremely alert worms, swimming readily and often of dark colour; most of the nereids live in semi-permanent burrows in mud or sand. The pharynx in most syllids, hesionids and nereids is directly related to the body wall by muscles acting both for protraction and retraction, although most

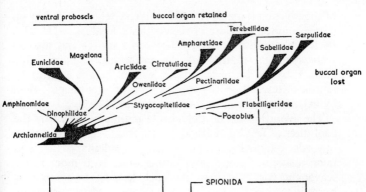

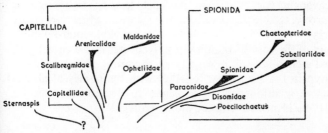

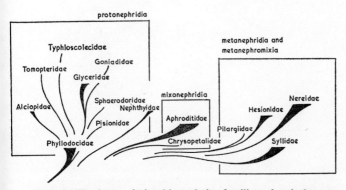

FIG. 9. The inter-relationships of the families of polychaetes. The Eunicidae and Aphroditidae are shown *in sensu lato* for clarity. After Dales[40]

of the everting force is, as in all polychaetes, provided by an increase in the pressure of the coelomic fluid (figs. 5D, 5E). In the phyllodocid-nephthyid-glycerid series, and also in scaleworms, retraction of the proboscis is more often affected by the intrinsic muscles within the gut wall, or by muscles attached to the buccal tube or oesophagus, than by extrinsic pharyngeal muscles (fig. 5F).

The evolution of the Polychaeta is thus mirrored by the evolution of feeding methods; a transition in one direction towards burrowing, tube building, sedentary life and microphagous feeding; and in the other to a more active scavenging or predatory existence leading to temporary burrowers, crevice-dwellers and worms which are truly pelagic throughout their lives. The probable inter-relationship of the various families of polychaetes is shown in fig. 9, and a classification in which they are grouped into orders is given in the Appendix, together with the names of all the genera mentioned in these pages. In Britain most species may be identified with the aid of Fauvel.[55]

4

THE VASCULAR SYSTEM AND
RESPIRATION

IMAGINE a spherical organism. Growth causing an increase in diameter will result in a decrease in the ratio of the surface area to volume. Since respiratory exchange must be carried on at the surface, the size will be limited by the ability of the surface to meet the respiratory demands of the contained volume. One of the simplest ways of maintaining the surface-to-volume ratio is for the body to be extended as a cylinder; provided that the radius is constant, there may be an infinite increase in length without disturbing the ratio. Capitellids, often living under conditions of poor oxygen supply, may be immensely long as compared with their width. Some earthworms may attain a length of six to ten feet, but are no thicker than a man's thumb.

Increase in diameter not only decreases the surface-to-volume ratio but removes some tissues farther from the surface where respiratory exchange takes place. The effect of increasing size necessitates not only increase in surface area, but a mechanism for transporting the dissolved gases to and from the deeper layers. The first effect has led to a wide variety of gills whose main characteristic is one of high surface area; the second, the provision of a fluid circulating system between the gills and the remainder of the body. The evolution of the coelom which removed the gut from the body wall may also have prompted the elaboration of a vascular system.

Many annelids may be regarded as cylinders, and when small their respiratory needs may be met by diffusion across the general body surface. This is true of the earthworms in which the cylindrical body may be regarded as an adaptation to a burrowing life, the rate of respiratory exchange being enhanced by superficial capillaries in the epidermis. When worms live in conditions of low oxygen concentration, when the need for oxygen is great owing to activity, or when only part of the body is exposed to freely circulating water, then gills of some kind may be found. Marcus[109] showed that the gills of the freshwater oligochaete, *Aulophorus furcatus*, actually lengthen under conditions of poor oxygen supply.

The metamerism of the annelid body has led to a repetition of many gills though their development may vary from one end of the body to the other. In the Polychaeta the majority of gills are provided by the parapodia. Many nereids, for example, have the notopodial lobes expanded to form leaf-like structures over the back. Many Eunicida which live in tubes have the notopodia extended into arborescent processes, the most anterior being the largest and the most frequently exposed by partial extension of the worm from its tube; *Diopatra* is a particularly beautiful example.

Not all gills, however, are related to the parapodia, though they may be segmentally arranged and dorso-lateral in position. The cirratulids have elongate filaments which serve a respiratory function and which arise from a large number of segments; terebellids have up to three pairs of tufted or arborescent gills on the most anterior segments, and some amphinomids have short, though often quite elaborate, gills all over the back. In sabellids and serpulids the prostomial crown has not only a feeding function but serves for respiration as well. These are but a few of the many kinds that have been evolved.

All these gills are well supplied with vessels and the position and arrangement of the gill areas often profoundly modify the vascular pattern. Basically the vascular system in annelids consists of a series of segmental vessels joining two longitudinal vessels running from one end of the body to the other; one in the mid-dorsal line in which the blood flows forward, and one in the corresponding ventral position in which the blood flows in the opposite direction. The ventral vessel lies just below the gut and dorsal to the nerve cord, beneath which a smaller (subneural) vessel is sometimes to be found. The ventral vessel gives rise to vessels in each segment supplying the epidermis and body-wall muscles. The vessels to the body wall may branch into a fairly complex system including vessels to the gills or to a subepidermal or epidermal plexus, the blood being eventually collected into the dorsal vessel by lateral vessels in each segment. The ventral vessel receives blood from the capillaries surrounding the gut which is supplied from the dorsal vessel by a vessel in each segment. This pattern has been somewhat modified in the more specialized annelids. Before considering these specializations we may perhaps illustrate the basic pattern by describing the vascular system in *Nereis*.[101], [123]

The vascular system in polychaetes

In *Nereis* the vascular system conforms to the plan just described, the principal modifications being in the anterior part of the body, which are due mainly to the development of the proboscis. Here the vessels connecting the dorsal and ventral vessels form a loose network. Respiratory exchange takes place over the body surface, more particularly on the dorsal side, and especially across the leaf-like expansions of the parapodia. In each segment the afferent vessel to these areas arises, not from the ventral vessel, but mid-laterally from the gut sinus on each side, branching into a network of subepidermal capillaries (fig. 10). The blood from these is collected into an efferent branch joining the dorsal vessel. Connected to the segmental afferent branch, there is another, smaller, vessel which arises from the ventral vessel and supplies the deeper tissues of the body wall and parapodium of that side. There is no dorsal counterpart, and the finer branches end, not in capillaries connected to an efferent vessel, but in short blind-ending digitiform branches. These are highly contractile, and are perhaps the most interesting peculiarity of the annelid vascular system.

In *Nereis* there are no specialized hearts, but all the vessels are to some extent contractile, simple or somewhat branched, circularly arranged muscle fibres being wound round them. The main vessels maintaining circulation, however, are the dorsal vessel and the segmental vessels arising from the gut sinus and supplying the subepidermal capillaries. The circulation is often weak and depends to a large extent on the activity of the worm. The longitudinal flow in the dorsal and ventral vessels, despite appearances,

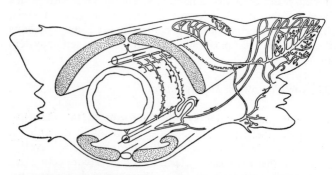

FIG. 10. The vascular system within a single segment of *Nereis virens*, looking forward. Based on Nicoll[123] and Lindroth[101]

is sluggish and is superimposed upon each segmental circuit. This is composed of a flow to and from the subepidermal respiratory plexus from which an ebb and flow is drawn to the deeper system by the other segmental vessels, and the highly contractile blind endings. In *N. virens* peristaltic contractions in the dorsal vessel normally commence at the posterior end and sweep forward. Injury or irritation at any point along the vessel sets up a new pacemaker from which waves may travel in both directions. Flow may stop and contractions can be reversed in any of the main contractile vessels. The waves propagated along the segmental vessels bear no relation to one another or to the longitudinal vessels; breaks in the continuity of the muscular coat may account for this. There may, however, be a rough co-ordination resulting from the draining effect of the dorsal vessel, and the whole system tends to keep itself going as distension of the vessel concerned excites the muscle fibres to contract.

In *Nephthys* most of the vessels are also contractile although the main propulsion is again due to the dorsal vessel. Nephthyids have sickle-shaped gills between the dorsal and ventral lobes of the parapodia, and these branchiae are supplied by vessels from the dorsal vessel. Each branchial vessel forms a loose coil within the gill and makes capillary connexions with another vessel running back to the ventral vessel in the neuropodial lobe. In addition to the ventral vessel, lateral neural vessels are also present and these give off paired branches in each segment. The segmental connexions between the ventral and dorsal vessels round the gut and the gut sinus are much simpler[24] than in *Nereis*, and the longitudinal circulation would appear to be better; not only are there lateral neural vessels, but there are more positive anterior links between the dorsal and ventral vessels. But the segmental supply to the muscles is surprisingly poor, and it may well be that the coelomic fluid is of particular importance in oxygen transport in these worms. It is interesting, therefore, to find that some nephthyids have haemoglobin in the coelomic fluid as well as in the blood.

In some polychaetes the vascular system is reduced or absent altogether. In the syllids this is perhaps related to their small size. In the scaleworms a vascular system is present in spite of a denial of its existence by many early investigators, the vessels being difficult to see owing to their delicacy and to the absence of pigment in the blood. In the glycerids the vascular system has disappeared, and haemoglobin-containing corpuscles are distributed in the coelomic fluid, the circulation of which is ensured by movements of the body-wall muscles and by tracts of ciliated peritoneum together with reduced septa. Again, while most terebellids have a well-developed vascular system, *Polycirrus* has none.

Another polychaete of which we know something of the pattern of circulation is *Arenicola marina*.[97] The two main longitudinal vessels are dorsal and ventral, but there are in addition smaller vessels on each side of the nerve cord and also more laterally placed along the line of the nephridia. The septa are absent throughout the branchial region, so that the afferent vessels arising from the ventral vessel and supplying the gills and nephridia, and the efferent vessels returning to the dorsal vessel, span the coelomic space. The gut is surrounded by a capillary network, which, as the worm ages, becomes a more and more complete sinus from which, however, the dorsal vessel and the ventral and lateral gastric vessels remain more or less distinct. At the anterior end of the intestine the lateral gastric vessel on each side is dilated to form an auricle entering the highly distensible ventricle of the heart which acts as a pump from the gastric sinus to the ventral vessel. While the dorsal vessel is commonly the most highly contractile vessel in polychaetes, the lateral hearts of *Arenicola* have no connexion with it and have presumably been evolved in response to the need to maintain a flow through the gut sinus. In polychaetes hearts tend to arise where there may be back pressure; in terebellids and ampharetids they are found behind the gills.

In large terebellids such as *Amphitrite johnstoni* the dorsal vessel seems to have disappeared in the region of the stomach and intestine and is functionally replaced by the lateral or paired ventral gastric vessels. These unite into an enormous dorsal vessel above the oesophagus, giving afferent branches to each of the gills.

As the gills are borne by the most anterior segments in *Amphitrite* the afferent branchial vessels arise from the dorsal vessel. In worms in which the gills are farther back, the blood may flow into the dorsal vessel from the gills.

The sabellids and serpulids have a more specialized

vascular system. In them the formation of small blind-ending vessels rather than through-flowing capillary net-works has been elaborated to such an extent that one may consider the vascular system to consist of a peripheral ebb-and-flow system, and a central system in which the blood flows in a more usual manner. In them there is a complete gut sinus, and, as in terebellids and ampharetids, the dorsal vessel has lost its identity except in the anterior oesophageal

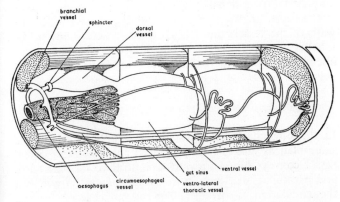

FIG. 11. The anterior vascular system of the serpulid, *Pomatoceros triqueter*, the crown removed. Redrawn from Hanson[74]

region where it forms a heart. This joins a ring vessel surrounding the oesophagus, supplying the crown and the ventral vessel. In serpulids, at the anterior end of the heart, just behind the junction with the ring vessel, is a sphincter muscle (fig. 11). This prevents backflow into the dorsal vessel so that, while blood passes forward from it to the crown, the blood ebbing from the crown is directed into the ventral vessel. In addition to the sphincter muscle, there is, at least in some serpulids, a horizontal septum which acts as a valve. There are many variations in detail between the species in which these structures are known,[74] and some of the smallest (*Spirorbis*, *Salmacina*) may lack both sphincter

and valve. Sabellids also lack sphincter and valve, and the
control of ebb and flow from the crown is somewhat
different.[54, 58] In *Sabella pavonina* it is merely the timing of
the pulsations of the branchial vessels which prevents the
same blood from being drawn back into the crown; the
branchial vessels remain contracted just long enough for
the blood which has been driven into them to be carried
away into the ventral vessel, so that on relaxation different
blood is drawn in from the dorsal vessel.[54] In terebellids,
ampharetids and flabelligerids there is loose, spongy tissue
in the heart, known as the 'heart-body', against which the
walls of the vessel contract. There is no heart-body in the
sabellid or serpulid heart, although intravasal tissues occur
elsewhere, both in the gut sinus and in the more posterior
vessels.[74]

The oligochaete vascular system

In the oligochaetes the vascular system is built on the
same plan as that of less specialized polychaetes: a dorsal
vessel conveys blood forward, a ventral vessel backward,
and a capillary network or sinus surrounds the gut. But
the circulation is stronger than in polychaetes, for the
segmental connexions between the dorsal and ventral
vessels are more direct and some of these are valved and act
as hearts. In *Tubifex* there is a single pair of such hearts, in
Lumbricus five.

In most oligochaetes respiratory exchange is simply
carried on at the body surface; few have special gills. The
superficial tissues are invaded by capillaries supplied from
the ventral vessel in earthworms, and these return blood to
the dorsal vessel. There are no blind-ending vessels as in
polychaetes, and the flow of blood is more efficiently directed
by the valved hearts, the valves consisting of ring-like flaps
of endothelium. As in polychaetes all the main vessels are
contractile, but the dorsal vessel and the lateral hearts
probably provide the main propulsive force. Not only are
the hearts valved, but valves may be found also at the

junctions of the segmental vessels with the dorsal vessel. In addition to the longitudinal dorsal and ventral vessels, a subneural vessel may also be of importance in some of the larger earthworms, providing, as it does, direct segmental links with the dorsal vessel. Lateral neural vessels may also be present.

External gills occur in some oligochaetes, the long posterior filaments of the tubificid *Branchiura sowerbyi* and the short tufted gills of the glossoscolecid *Alma eubranchiata* being notable examples. These are supplied by simple elongate loops from the ventral to the dorsal vessel.

The blood vessels of leeches

In the leeches the vascular system is apparently complicated by the invasion of the coelom by connective tissue, and by its restriction to a series of channels or sinuses. These form a kind of secondary vascular system, parts becoming contractile to maintain circulation. In some leeches this coelomic system nowhere connects with the true vascular system, yet may be important in respiration. In *Placobdella costata*, for example, there is a network of fine coelomic vessels beneath the epidermis.

The true blood vascular system in leeches is built on the same plan as that of oligochaetes in having a dorsal and aventral vessel joined by transverse vessels. While this vascular pattern is fundamentally segmental in arrangement, the loss of septa and consequent internal structural changes has enabled the arrangement of these transverse vessels to be distorted into a series of loops. In *Hemiclepsis*, for example, three pairs of long loop vessels arise from the dorsal vessel about halfway down the body; two of these loop forward to join the ventral vessel near its anterior end, the other loops backward almost as far as the posterior sucker, and then turns forward as a lateral vessel to join the ventral vessel with the others at the anterior end of the body. The most anterior of these loops projects into the anterior sucker itself, and the dorsal vessel also bifurcates anteriorly into the sucker to meet the ventral vessel just behind its posterior rim. Posteriorly the dorsal vessel gives off a series of loops radiating into the posterior sucker collecting blood from the hinder end of the ventral vessel.

The coelomic, lacunar, lymphatic or sinus system, as it is variously called, is superimposed on the true blood vascular system. It generally consists of a dorsal sinus which encloses the dorsal vessel, a ventral sinus enclosing the ventral vessel and nerve cord, and lateral sinuses (fig. 12). These lateral sinuses are often muscular and

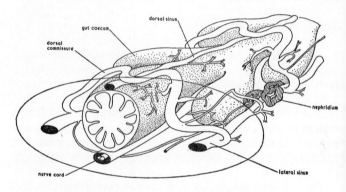

FIG. 12. The sinus system in a mid-body segment of the leech *Poecilobdella* (based on figures by Bhatia[6])

contractile. In *Piscicola*, superficial pulsatile vesicles occur at the junctions of the lateral sinuses with the transverse channels, and act as gills. In *Branchellion* these are extended into leaf-life structures. The dorsal vessel of *Piscicola* shows rhythmical contractions which serve not only to drive the blood forwards within the dorsal vessel, but by touching the inner walls of the dorsal coelomic sinus at diastole serve also to circulate the fluid in the surrounding sinus.

The inclusion of the dorsal and ventral blood vessels within the cavity of another system foreshadows the reduction of the true vascular system which is functionally replaced by the coelomic sinus system in many leeches. In *Erpobdella* the circulatory system consists of a ventral sinus joined to the lateral muscular vessel-like sinuses by paired vessels in each segment. In the posterior part of the body these are forked, each limb being dilated into a pulsatile vesicle. The lateral sinuses give rise to superficial dendritic branches related to respiratory exchange. The arrangement in *Hirudo* and in *Haemopis* is much the same as this, but in them there is also a dorsal sinus. In gnathobdellids the original vascular system has become entirely replaced by the coelomic sinus system which carries the haemoglobin of the blood. This replacement of one system by another is surely related to the obliteration of the segmental coelomic spaces separating the gut from the body wall in other annelids.

The blood

All these circulatory systems have a dual function: first to convey oxygen to the tissues and to remove carbon dioxide, and secondly to transport nutrients and waste products of metabolism. Most annelids are marine, but as we have seen already there are a number that live in fresh water and in the soil on land. The amount of oxygen which dissolves in water depends on the partial pressure of the gas and decreases with rising temperature and rising salt content. At 15°C there is normally about 7 cc of oxygen/litre in fresh water; in sea water only 5·8 cc/1 oxygen will dissolve in the blood plasma to the extent of about 5·8 cc oxygen/1 at 15°C, but the amount which the blood can carry is enhanced by solution in the blood of compounds such as haemoglobin. Worms do not have much haemoglobin as compared with vertebrates, perhaps a quarter of the concentration in man, but *Arenicola marina*, for example, has enough to increase the oxygen capacity of its blood tenfold.

The blood of the smallest annelids is usually colourless: their needs for oxygen may be met by simple diffusion and physical solution; but a respiratory pigment, or pigments, is usually present in larger worms. In most this is hae-moglobin, but in sabellids, serpulids, flabelligerids and some ampharetids it is a greenish allied compound, chloro-cruorin. *Magelona* has another pigment, haemerythrin, appar-ently similar to that of sipunculids. The blood of *Serpula* has a brown colour as it contains both haemoglobin and chlorocruorin. These pigments are composed of a protein (which varies from one species to another) and an iron porphyrin (haem) compound. In haemoglobin the haem is the red protohaem, in chlorocruorin it is the green chlorocruorohaem.[57] Haemerythrin does not contain a por-phyrin.

We know little about the tissues which actually elaborate the plasma pigments. In polychaetes with heart-bodies there is good evidence that haematopoiesis occurs there, and there is some indication that tissues referred to as 'chlora-gogen' in polychaetes may also participate in this process; certainly the darkly pigmented cells clothing the blind-ending vessels in *Arenicola marina* have heavy concentra-tions of haemoglobin precursors,[95] and of ferritin.[183]

One common characteristic of chlorocruorin and of worm haemoglobins in the plasma is the very large size of the molecules which have molecular weights round three million. These molecules are so large in *Arenicola* that Roche[133a] and his colleagues in Paris have been able to make electron photomicrographs in which their 6-unit hexagonal structure can be clearly seen within the 'chloragogen' cells. This size tends to contain the pigment within the vessels, and also maintains the colloid osmotic pressure of the blood; vertebrates have additional proteins for this, but these are sparse or lacking in worms. When these pigments occur within corpuscles (as in capitellids, in *Terebella lapidaria*, *Travisia forbesii*, *Glycera* and *Magelona*) the molecular weight is much lower; in *Magelona* the haemery-thrin has a molecular weight of 66,000, much the same as that of human corpuscular haemoglobin; the molecular weight in *Glycera* corpuscles is 68,000. In most worms, however, the haemoglobin is in solution in the blood, giving it a bright red colour in contrast to the colourless coelomic fluid. When haemoglobin is found in the coelomic fluid, as in species with degenerate vascular systems such as *Glycera* or *Polycirrus haematodes*, it usually occurs in corpuscles. *Nephthys hombergii*, however, has one kind of haemoglobin dissolved in the blood plasma, and another in the coelomic fluid.[91]

While the presence of these pigments increases the oxygen capacity of the blood, the use of the pigment to the worm depends on the properties of the particular haemoglobin. This must not be confused with the total oxygen capacity of the blood, which will depend on the quantity of pigment it contains. Each haemoglobin has its own characteristic oxygen-dissociation curve. These curves are all more or less sigmoid in shape, but differ in slope, that is, in the percentage saturation at different concentrations of oxygen (fig. 13). That of *Arenicola marina* reaches a high degree of saturation at low concentrations. This means that the

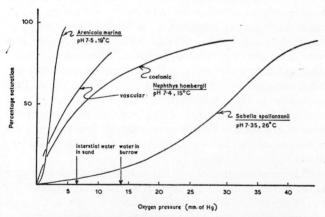

FIG. 13. Oxygen-dissociation curves of the haemoglobin of *Arenicola marina* and *Nephthys hombergii* (from Jones[91]), and of the chlorocruorin from *Sabella spallanzanii* (from Fox[57]). The pressure of oxygen in the water in the *Arenicola* burrow and in the interstitial water in the sand are after 5 hr exposure (from Jones[91])

haemoglobin is capable of picking up oxygen at low concentrations and, as shown by the steepness of the curve, of unloading it to the tissues. The haemoglobin of *Tubifex* also has a high oxygen affinity which helps the worm to live under conditions of poor oxygen supply.[44] The chlorocruorin of *Sabella spallanzanii*, on the other hand, can pick up little oxygen at low outside concentrations and is capable of functioning only under conditions of high oxygen concentration, and the haemoglobin of *Serpula* has as low an affinity for oxygen as the chlorocruorin mixed with it.

There is also another factor of importance influencing the ability of animals to make use of oxygen when this is present in very low concentration: that of pH. Increasing acidity may shift the oxygen-dissociation curve to the right (a positive Bohr effect), or to the left (a negative Bohr effect). A shift to the right means that less oxygen may be taken up by the blood at a given concentration. A haemoglobin showing no Bohr effect, or better still a negative Bohr effect, would thus be valuable to an animal which might at times be subjected to a low pH as a result of accumulation of carbon dioxide, such as might occur in a burrow at low tide. *Arenicola marina* haemoglobin has a slight positive Bohr effect, but this worm is probably less often subjected to high carbon-dioxide concentrations than some others. The oligochaete swampworm, *Alma emini*, is perhaps the most tolerant of any worm of high concentrations of carbon dioxide, for the oxygen-loading ability of the blood is unaffected by concentrations of 30% carbon dioxide by volume in air.[9]

Chlorocruorin in *Sabella* has a low affinity for oxygen at low concentrations, but there is no reason to suppose that all chlorocruorins have this feature. We do not know anything about the characteristics of chlorocruorins in flabelligerids or ampharetids, but as these often live under foul conditions one might predict that their chlorocruorins are better adapted than those of sabellids to load oxygen at low concentrations.

Respiratory exchange

Both haemoglobin and chlorocruorin can be demonstrated to have a real value in oxygen transport by measuring the rate of oxygen uptake in a normal worm and in the same animal in which the pigment is prevented from functioning by previous treatment with carbon monoxide. Bearing in mind the oxygen-dissociation characteristics, experiments can be done to test whether the pigment is of greater use in some conditions than in others. Jürgens[93] found in *Nereis diversicolor*, for example, that oxygen uptake was reduced by half at high oxygen concentrations, and reduced completely at low, although it must be mentioned that he was working with narcotized animals. Similarly, Johnson[90] found that the haemoglobin in the earthworm, *Lumbricus terrestris*, carries about 40% of the oxygen it uses under normal conditions. Dausend[44] also found that the oxygen uptake was less in carbon-monoxide-treated *Tubifex*, and in all well-investigated instances the haemoglobin does act as a carrier of oxygen down to outside concentrations at which it can still be loaded. The pigment may be of 'use', of course, only at lower oxygen concentrations if the needs can be met by the amount in physical solution under more normal circumstances.

Another function of haemoglobin in worms has been suggested: that of storage of oxygen to be used during periods of severe oxygen lack, or under anaerobic conditions. Such conditions are probably endured by many worms, but in all instances examined in detail the oxygen-storing capacity of the blood has been found to be too low to be of much use. While glycogen may be used at such times, lactic acid does not accumulate so that there is no increase in oxygen uptake to pay off an oxygen debt following an anaerobic period. This is certainly true of *Arenicola marina* and *Owenia fusiformis*, both of which can withstand long periods of strictly anaerobic conditions, *Owenia* for as long as three weeks. They live on glycogen, but generally conserve their resources by a reduction of activity.[36] Ralph's work[131] on *Lumbricus terrestris*, however, suggests that oxygen debts may be incurred by the earthworm. He found that oxygen uptake followed a regular cycle, being greater during the late evening than midday, and that this did not coincide with a similar diurnal activity cycle. At some times oxygen uptake was greater when the worm was quiescent than at others when it was actively moving about. This could be of great adaptive significance, for it might enable a worm to burrow in soil with little available oxygen.

Barcroft and Barcroft were among the first to suggest that the haemoglobin of the blood might have an oxygen-storing function, though this idea was later abandoned.[52] They found that in *Arenicola marina* an oxygen capacity of 5·7–8·7 vols % of the total blood volume, Borden[52] 8·4–9·7 vols %, and she calculated that there was sufficient oxygen to last 70 minutes. Animals of about 10 g (fresh) weight respire at a rate of about 0·25 cc oxygen/g/hr at normal temperatures. If an oxygen capacity of 9 vols % be taken, and the blood volume is 0·3 ml/g, then a 10 g

worm will have $10 \times 0.3 \times \dfrac{9}{100} = 0.27$ cc oxygen, which

will last only $\dfrac{60}{2.5} \times 0.27$ or approximately $6\frac{1}{2}$ minutes.

Eliassen[52] found the store lasted for between one-half and seven minutes. Jones[91] found in *Nephthys hombergii* that the oxygen store would also last for only a few minutes. Such stores are clearly insufficient to provide for the time that many worms may be subjected to very low oxygen concentrations, although the oxygen uptake may be greatly reduced under such conditions by reduction of activity. While many live in mud in which there may be little or no oxygen, many irrigate their burrows. When the burrows are uncovered by the tide, some resort to aerial respiration, while others trap bubbles of air in the water remaining within the burrow. On the other hand, the oxygen content of the water in *Arenicola* burrows and in the interstitial water in the sand was found by Jones[91] not to fall lower than the concentration at which the haemoglobin would no longer function.

Leeches are often found in stagnant pools under conditions of very poor oxygen supply, when more haemoglobin is produced by *Erpobdella carena*. Some leeches, however, merely leave the water under such conditions to respire in air, though many can survive several days without oxygen. Among oligochaetes the abilities of *Tubifex* to withstand oxygen-lack are well known, and Alsterberg[3] and Dausend[44] suggested that anaerobic metabolism of glycogen may on such occasions be important. Von Brand[16] found a higher glycogen consumption in *Sabella spallanzanii* and *Halla parthenopeia* under anaerobic conditions than when aerated.

Most annelids seem able to maintain their respiratory rate down to fairly low oxygen concentrations (generally to about 2 cc oxygen/l). Mann[108] has found that whereas the rate of oxygen consumption is dependent on concentration in *Erpobdella octoculata* and *Piscicola geometra*, *Helobdella stagnalis*, which, as its name implies, is often found under conditions of poor oxygen supply, can to some extent regulate the rate of oxygen uptake, and *Glossiphonia complanata* can also do so down to a concentration as low as 1·5 cc oxygen/l. *Erpobdella testacea* can also do it after acclimatization to lowered oxygen concentration; haemoglobin plays no part in this.

Whether uptake of oxygen through the gut is important is still a controversial matter; in many instances there is little evidence for it, but it may perhaps be important in some freshwater oligochaetes. There is also some evidence, from Watson's[158] observations on *Pectinaria*, that the scapha at the hind end of the body may be concerned with respiration. Some hesionid polychaetes gulp gas bubbles produced by algae.

In most instances, however, oxygen uptake takes place over the body surface, more particularly across regions specialized to act as gills, and many worms cause currents to flow across them by one means or another. Many polychaetes have essentially U-shaped burrows or have tubes with both inhalant and exhalant apertures for this reason. Nevertheless, *Arenicola marina* is able to irrigate its L-shaped burrow, for the water drawn in at the tail end seeps away. Worms such as *Nephthys* with temporary burrows, and *Sabella pavonina* with tubes leading straight down into the mud or sand, also do this,[163] water entering from the top and seeping away at the bottom. *Sabella spallanzanii* and many other sabellids, on the other hand, have tubes with a freely open hind end, and irrigation may be carried on in either direction.[163, 37]

The irrigation current is often produced by muscular means. Piston-like swellings pass up or down the body in *Arenicola marina*, in terebellids and sabellids; nereids undulate the body in the dorso-ventral plane. Many leeches also undulate their bodies in a similar manner. In *Tubifex* the part of the body exposed above the surface of the mud performs corkscrew-like writhing movements. Scaleworms produce an irrigation current over the back by movement of the elytra and the back itself. This was studied by van Dam[41] in *Aphrodite* and *Hermione*. He found that the current passed between the parapodia into a space between the body wall and the elytra, and escaped near the posterior end of the body which was held up to the surface of the sand. In some other polychaetes such as *Nephthys*, spionids and sabellariids, irrigation is ciliary. *Nephthys* maintains a stream over the sickle-shaped gills in the notch between the parapodial lobes in this way, and spionids have bands of long cilia mid-dorsally in each segment.

Most polychaetes withdraw 50–60% of the oxygen in the water they pass over their bodies. Van Dam measured the quantity of water pumped by *Arenicola*, by acclimatizing a worm to a glass tube immersed in a tank maintained at constant level. The tube was connected to a small vessel in which the water level was the same as that in the tank, so that water pumped in that direction by the worm overflowed into a measuring cylinder. During a burst of irrigation about 90 ml was pumped in 10 minutes by a worm of average size.

In two terebellids (*Thelepus crispus* and *Eupolymnia heterobranchia*) the volume pumped under the same conditions was directly related to the respiratory rate of each; in *Eupolymnia* the rate of oxygen uptake was found to be twice that of *Thelepus* and it pumped water through the burrow at twice the rate, the percentage utilization of oxygen being much the same.[38]

All these worms irrigate intermittently, pausing from time to time. Lindroth[101] found in *Nereis virens* that irrigation became continuous at low oxygen concentrations (2 cc oxygen/1) but was liable to stop when very low (0·6 cc/1). In *Arenicola marina* pauses are neither shortened nor abolished at low oxygen concentrations, and in well-aerated water periods of irrigation alternate with pauses of clockwork regularity. Wells[162] has studied this in some detail and has brought forward good evidence that such rhythmic behaviour is controlled by an internal pacemaker and that the resumption of irrigation after each pause is not due to external conditions such as carbon-dioxide accumulation or oxygen-lack in the burrow. Such cyclical behaviour would be especially useful under conditions when the burrow is covered by water made noxious by rising temperature or other factors, owing to tidal exposure. Irrigation would then cease, but the worm would make occasional 'testing' bursts of irrigation until more favourable conditions returned. *Nereis diversicolor*[167] and the sabellid *Schizobranchia insignis*[37] react in much the same way.

While many polychaetes irrigating their tubes have specialized gills, a considerable part of the total oxygen uptake may take place across the general body surface. The sabellids form a rather special case, for here the vascularized crown acts both as a gill and as a filter-feeding organ. *Myxicola infundibulum* lives in a slimy tube closed at the hind end; it does not irrigate its tube and is wholly dependent on the crown for oxygen. *Sabella pavonina* and *S. spallanzanii* both irrigate their tubes by muscular swellings passing down the body. Zoond[164] measured the oxygen uptake after amputation of the crown in *Bispira* and found a

60% fall; Fox[57] found much the same order of decrease when *Sabella spallanzanii* was similarly treated. The ciliated crown probably consumes a substantial part of the total oxygen uptake in its own activity, for Wells[163] found that the sum of the rates of uptake of the parts after bisection of *S. pavonina* did not differ much from the normal animal. If the crown is amputated the body continues to live and to regenerate a new crown provided it can irrigate; but in a normal animal the crown can provide the oxygen required by the whole body when irrigation is prevented.[37] It was shown that in *Schizobranchia* oxygen uptake was some 40% lower when the worm was completely withdrawn within the tube and allowed to irrigate, but that the worm could maintain its rate of uptake when irrigation was prevented. Further, measurement of the amount of water pumped through the tube by the activity of the body amounted to about 12 ml/g (fresh weight) hr at 12–13°C while under the same conditions the crown passed 70 ml/g/hr by ciliary activity. Much of the oxygen taken up by the crown will be used for its own purposes. The large volume of water passed through the crown results in a low utilization of oxygen (10%), and a higher utilization (24%) is reached when the worm is wholly withdrawn within its tube. Clearly the large volume passed through the crown is related to feeding rather than respiration.

Aerial respiration may be carried on by many intertidal polychaetes whenever the water level falls below the burrow openings. *Arenicola marina* does this, and *Nereis diversicolor* also does so by trapping bubbles between the body and the burrow walls. *Nereis* crawls up the burrow until the head emerges from the water when undulatory waves of the usual irrigatory pattern commence and pass backward, thereby trapping a series of bubbles. When the first of these reaches the hind end movements cease abruptly, holding the bubbles in position. After some minutes the bubbles are released and the process repeated. *Thoracophelia mucronata*, the bloodworm of Californian beaches, comes to the surface when the tide is out, and by making a funnel-like depression in the sand exposes the hind part of the body, so that the rectum may act as a lung. The African swampworm *Alma emini* also backs up to the surface. It has an area of the hinder part of the body highly vascularized and this may be rolled up also to act as a kind of lung.[9] There is one danger of such variable conditions, and that is of the worm facing higher oxygen concentrations than those to which it is accustomed, which could be harmful.

Earthworms respire through the vascularized epidermis which is kept moist with mucus or possibly by fluid from the dorsal pores. Normally there is an adequate supply of oxygen in the soil, but this may be reduced if waterlogging occurs after rain. The importance of the epidermal capillaries in respiration has been confirmed, for oxygen uptake was increased when they were dilated by adrenalin, and decreased when constricted by acetylcholine—the reverse effect, incidentally, of these drugs on vertebrate capillaries.[110] These experiments were made with *Pheretima*, *Glossoscolex* and *Pontoscolex*. Some leeches may be found hanging on foliage, especially in tropical rain forests where the humidity is high and ultraviolet-ray penetration poor.

Many of the physiological problems of respiration in annelids, which have only been mentioned here, require further study. In this chapter we have considered one aspect only of the body fluids, that of transport of oxygen and carbon dioxide in respiration. In the next chapter we shall consider the regulation of its other constituents, and the participation of both blood and coelomic fluid in the elimination of wastes.

D

5

EXCRETION AND REGULATION
OF THE BODY FLUIDS

IN MOST annelids there are two fluid-filled systems, the coelom and the vascular system; in most species these are separate. In a few polychaetes, such as capitellids, glycerids and *Polycirrus* amongst terebellids, the blood system has disappeared, while in leeches the coelom has become restricted to a system of vessels with the growth of connective tissue. The coelomic fluid and the blood, while remaining separate in most annelids, may contain haemoglobin in solution or in corpuscles. Both the coelomic fluid and the blood participate in the transmission of absorbed nutrients and in the elimination of waste.

The metanephridial funnels or protonephridial soleno-cytes lie in the coelomic fluid and discharge to the outside. But the fluid which issues from the nephridiopores of an earthworm does not have the same composition as the coelomic fluid. It has a high proportion of nitrogenous waste, notably ammonia and urea, and its osmotic pressure is considerably lower.

Nitrogenous excretion in earthworms

Lesser kept earthworms immersed in water for one day. In this water he found ammonia, but no urea.[6] Delaunay, by extending immersion for a week, found not only ammonia, but also urea and amines.[6] Bahl found that he could drain fluid from a pile of over one hundred *Pheretima posthuma* kept on an inclined plane in a moist chamber. After two and a half hours, 25 ml had collected, and this contained 0·68 mg ammonia, 0·80 mg urea, 0·12 mg creatinine and a large quantity of protein probably derived from the mucus exuded by the skin.[6] Wolf[173] estimated the rate of urine flow of *Lumbricus* to equal 60% of the body weight per day. Needham[113] has shown that about half the nitrogen lost from the body is contained in the mucus. As in some vertebrates, the proportion of ammonia to urea in the urine varies according to the physiological condition of the animal. Needham found that in *Lumbricus terrestris* there is an increase in acid production during feeding which is neutralized by an increased production of ammonia and a decrease in urea. This would explain Lesser's failure to detect urea after only twenty-four hours, whereas Delaunay found appreciable quantities after a week. After feeding, the decrease in urea is greater than the increase in ammonia, so that the pathways leading to these two substances may be independent. *Lumbricus* and *Allolobophora* are similar in these respects, but *Eisenia foetida* is different. In *Eisenia*, ammonia increases when the animal is fasting, and Needham suggests that the acids produced in feeding are neutralized by calcium carbonate from the calciferous glands.

From this we may perhaps expect some variation in the proportion of the various excretory end products in annelids, but it would appear that ammonia and urea are the predominant ones. Both are very soluble, and only traces of relatively insoluble substances such as uric acid are present. Although Florkin and Duchateau found no uricotelic enzymes in *Lumbricus*, they did find xanthine oxidase. Cohen and Lewis found traces of uric acid in *Lumbricus terrestris* and traces have also been found in *Arenicola marina* (0.1 mg/100 ml of coelomic fluid) and *Chaetopterus* (0.73 mg/100 ml).[6, 113, 114]

Most of these determinations of nitrogenous substances have been made either on coelomic fluid or from water in which the animals have been immersed. Bahl,[6] however, has estimated urea, ammonia and creatinine in the blood as well as in the coelomic fluid to see which was the more important in conveying these substances. He found that in *Pheretima posthuma* the urea content of blood and coelomic fluid was similar, but that the blood contained more ammonia and creatinine that the coelomic fluid. Bahl made determinations of these substances in the body wall and in the gut wall, and found that the intestine yielded more ammonia, over twice as much urea, but distinctly less creatinine, than the body wall. Cohen's and Lewis's[113, 114] finding that in *Lumbricus* arginase activity was related to urea output suggests that urea is produced in the same way as in vertebrates. They also found a higher arginase activity in homogenates of the gut wall than in those from the body wall, and that feeding with either arginine or citrulline augmented urea production; of these arginine was the more effective. Abdel-Fattah[1] also reported augmented urea output in *Lumbricus* when worms were fed amino acids alone, but Cohen and Lewis did not find this, though they concluded that arginase activity was low in the body wall of *Lumbricus*, and that most, if not all, of the activity was in the gut. This supports Bahl's analyses of gut wall. On the other hand, the body wall of *Eisenia foetida* contains a large proportion of its total urea, and while in *Lumbricus* more urea is found in the gut wall than in the body wall, the amount found there is still appreciable.[114]

It is not possible to tell from these observations whether the excretory products found in the urine are derived from both the blood and the coelomic fluid, or from the coelomic fluid alone. Bahl found quantitative differences between the nitrogenous compounds of the blood and coelomic fluid, but the quantities present in the urine and in the coelomic fluid were not markedly different. In *Pheretima* there are small dilatations in the capillary network on the nephridium which Bahl thought might act like glomeruli, but these could be concerned with water or salt absorption from the nephridium rather than with nitrogenous excretion. Bahl[6] found, somewhat surprisingly, that the urine contained less creatinine than the blood, and thought that this must be due to resorption from the nephridium, although this does not necessarily follow. The similar urea and ammonia contents of the coelomic fluid and urine suggest that the nephridia are acting merely as drains. The ammonia and urea in the urine could be derived from the coelomic fluid or directly from the blood by diffusion through the nephridial capillaries.

The nephridia of the earthworm appear to function also for storage of other waste materials. After injection of ink or other particles into the coelom, the particles are taken up by the middle tube of the nephridium. Dark brown particles apparently accumulate there throughout life, the increase in quantity with age suggesting a permanent deposition and an inability to eliminate them. Some of these granules, though not necessarily all, may be derived from the blood, since Bahl[6] found them to be haemoglobin derivatives—they are certainly not guanine as Willem and Minne thought.[6] Bahl suggested that in *Pheretima* this site of particle uptake might prevent clogging of the tube.

The chloragocytes and other peritoneal cells

Abdel-Fattah[1] suggested that the high concentrations of urea found in the wall of the earthworm gut were due to activity of the chloragocytes. In most books the chloragocytes of earthworms are described as cells directly associated with the blood vessels of the gut, containing yellow or yellow-brown granules, the chloragosomes. Opinion differs as to whether the granules are shed, or whether the whole cell breaks free into the coelom, but in either case the chloragosomes are described as being conveyed to the outside by the nephridia. There is certainly no evidence whatever that this occurs. The function of the chloragocytes in earthworms has recently been investigated from several viewpoints. It seems that the chloragocytes are concerned not only with nitrogen metabolism, but also with storage and metabolism of oil and glycogen. This duality of function partly reconciles the two apparently opposing views that 1, the cells were excretory, and 2, concerned with food storage. There are many controversial points still to be settled, however, and much of the confusion may be due to some analyses having been made of the whole wall of the gut, not of the chloragocytes alone. It is now clear that the true chloragocyte contains both yellow granules and deposits of oil and glycogen. The chloragosomes have a complicated structure and would be termed 'calculi' in medicine. Van Gansen and Vandermeerssche[64] have shown quite clearly that these granules are built up from a number of concentric layers. Van Gansen[61] working with *Allolobophora caliginosa* has found good evidence that these layers consist of the purine heteroxanthine and the silicate muscovite, together with a yellow lipid pigment. However, Roots[134] working with *Lumbricus terrestris* chloragosomes found, by element analysis, only 4% nitrogen, concluding that the chloragosomes probably consist almost entirely of phospholipid together with a yellow pigment of uncertain composition. There seems general agreement that the main role of the chloragocytes is storage and metabolism of oil and glycogen, and though they produce urea and ammonia this is not their main function. Liebmann proposed that the chloragocytes were mainly concerned with lipid metabolism, and brought much evidence forward to support this view.[156] Urich[156] has confirmed these ideas by quantitative determinations of oil after feeding with olive oil and fatty acids, and by studying the effect of fasting. It may be added that van Gansen has also found glucose–1–phosphate, a phosphorylase and an acid phosphatase in the chloragocytes.

The fate of the chloragocytes is still not clear, but it seems more likely that the whole cell, not just the chloragosomes, disintegrates into the coelomic fluid. The chloragosomes are then taken up by amoebocytes; these gradually accumulate to form the 'brown bodies' which increase in size and number with age—there is no evidence that they are ever eliminated.

Very little is known about nitrogenous excretion in polychaetes. Cells often referred to as chloragocytes are perhaps not comparable with those of oligochaetes. Groups of cells directly related to vessels are found in polychaetes, but they are limited in distribution and the only analyses that have been made show them to contain large quantities of haemoglobin precursors and breakdown products.[95] The metabolic functions of the earthworm chloragocytes seem to be fulfilled by other cells, by cells covering the gut, bordering the coelom, or those derived from the peritoneum and lying freely in the coelomic fluid. The haematopoietic function of the cells attached to the blood vessels does not preclude them acting also as 'kidneys of accumulation'. The heart-bodies of terebellids and some other polychaetes, which consist of spongy masses of tissue lying inside the lumen of the dorsal vessel, are comparable with such cells which have become involuted.

Most annelids have free cells in the coelom derived from the peritoneum. They may be of more than one kind, and may have more than one use, but often apparently different kinds represent stages in the growth of a single type. Most are phagocytic and may become loaded with excretory matter or food or with foreign substances artificially introduced into the coelom. But they are not necessarily confined to the coelom for the more actively amoebocytic cells may pass into the gut or skin.

In sabellids such as *Sabella spallanzanii* there are free coelomocytes derived from the peritoneum. In some other sabellids such as *Eudistylia polymorpha* and *Schizobranchia insignis*, for example, there are few free cells, but the peritoneum itself is elaborated into villi projecting into the coelom. Both the free cells of *Sabella* and the villous cells of *Eudistylia* and *Schizobranchia* contain large quantities of glycogen and oil. These reserves seem destined for the gametes; and, if worms are made to fast, reserves in the body wall or gut are drawn upon rather than those in the coelom.[39]

In the leeches it may be remembered that the coelom has been invaded by connective tissue within which two other tissues proliferate as the animal ages. One is the botryoidal tissue which often takes the form of grape-like proliferations of the wall of the vessels, the other the vaso-fibrous tissue which is formed by expansions of the cells of the finer branches of the sinus walls. Both systems become gradually loaded with pigment with increasing age.[15] The botryoidal tissue of *Hirudo* has a characteristic brown colour, and consists of a masked iron compound probably derived from blood. The vaso-fibrous cells contain a green pigment, possibly a bile pigment of similar derivation. Both tissues could be described as 'kidneys of accumulation'. In *Glossiphonia*, on the other hand, the function of both botryoidal and vaso-fibrous tissues appears to be assumed by adipose cells lying in the connective tissue.[15]

We know very little about nitrogenous excretion in leeches, although *Hirudo* is known to produce mostly ammonia together with relatively smaller quantities of urea and traces of other wastes. Büsing *et al*[21] have presented evidence that some of this ammonia may be produced from more complex nitrogenous substances by bacteria in the nephridial capsules. In most leeches the restriction of the coelom has resulted in the nephridial funnel opening into an ampulla. The capsular expansion of the tubule just behind the funnel may also contain amoebocytes. Blood vessels commonly supply both ampulla and capsule and surround them with botryoidal cells.

Regulation of water and salts

The nephridia in annelids do then convey ammonia, urea and other nitrogenous waste to the outside, but as yet there is no evidence that they actively excrete these substances. There is more evidence, however, for an osmoregulatory function. Ramsay[132] has shown that in *Lumbricus terrestris* the urine has an osmotic pressure lower than that of the blood and coelomic fluid under natural conditions, and that the ability to form a hyposmotic urine is confined to the wide tube and possibly also to the middle tube of the nephridium. Bahl[6] found much less chloride in the urine than in the coelomic fluid in *Pheretima posthuma* (50 mg/100 ml in the blood as compared with 80 mg/100 ml in the coelomic fluid).

In *Lumbricus terrestris* the osmotic pressure of the coelomic fluid is always higher than that of the external medium, but the chloride content is only higher when the concentration of the medium is less than 0·35% NaCl.[132] At all higher concentrations it is less. While the earthworm is similar to freshwater animals in that the osmotic pressure of the coelomic fluid increases with that of the medium, it shares with the *Aedes* mosquito larva the ability to keep down the concentration of chloride ions when the concentration in the medium is high. It does not follow, however, that there is an active excretion of chloride ions against the concentration gradient, for water will at the same time be entering the body owing to the increased internal osmotic pressure, so that the net effect may well be one of dilution of coelomic fluid. The chloride content of the coelomic fluid may then be maintained at a level lower than that of the medium, and the urine could still be hyposmotic. Both water and salt probably enter passively through the skin at all concentrations except in fresh water, when there is an active salt uptake and there is an active secretion of an hyposmotic urine under all circumstances. When an earthworm is placed in fresh water its weight increases owing to osmotic inflow, when urine flow also increases; they can live indefinitely when submerged. Worms may come to the surface after heavy rain from oxygen-lack rather than from a need to escape osmotic effects of flooding. Water enters through the skin, not by the mouth or anus. Partly desiccated worms will rapidly increase in weight when replaced in moist soil or water. It is not known whether water as well as salt is resorbed by the nephridia, and although Bahl[6] suggested that the elongate tubule in *Pheretima posthuma* may be an adaptation for water resorption, his quantitative determinations of ammonia and urea in urine and coelomic fluid suggest that it is not. *Pheretima* and some other drought-resisting earthworms have some nephridia opening into the gut (chapter 1) and it may be that these are adaptations for better water conservation.

The leeches are also a predominantly freshwater group

D*

though some have become terrestrial in the sense that they may be found hanging from foliage in tropical or subtropical forests. Some leeches can withstand more drying than other annelids. Oka,[67] for example, notes the remarkable resistance of *Ozobranchus jantseanus* which attacks the turtle *Clemmys japonica*. These leeches can withstand a loss of four-fifths of their total weight as a result of drying while the turtle basks in the sun. The leeches can be left in air for a week when they dry up to an apparently amorphous mass; but an hour and a half in water is sufficient to restore their weight and activity. Marine leeches parasitizing fish have undoubtedly become secondarily adapted to salt water, but we know little about their osmotic relations with the medium. It would seem that, as in earthworms, the urine may be very dilute and that the epidermis has an ability to take up ions against the gradient. Perhaps the skin is less permeable, or like elasmobranch fishes they have an enhanced urea content. Few oligochaetes are found on the sea-shore and these are more estuarine than marine in habit; the majority of oligochaetes are quite intolerant of a high concentration of salt.

Several polychaetes can tolerate low external salt concentration enabling them to live in estuaries. This does not necessarily imply that they are capable of osmoregulation, but only a capacity to tolerate a reduction of the salt content of their own body fluids as a consequence of osmotic inflow, and an ability to pump the water out again by the nephridia. Schlieper,[137] for example, showed that in *Arenicola marina* the osmotic pressure of the body fluid followed passively that of the medium, but that worms were able to tolerate a low salt concentration in the blood; those living in the Kiel Canal had half the value of those in Heligoland.

Some polychaetes are found in estuaries and a few even in fresh water. Most of these are nereids and sabellids. Well-known examples are *Nereis limnicola* in California, and the sabellids *Dybowscella* of Lake Baikal and *Manayunkia speciosa* in Lake Erie. There are also a few rare instances of polychaetes which have become terrestrial. Several species of *Nereis* and *Lycastis* burrow in soil in Sumatra, and are found in axils of the leaves or decaying wood of various palms.

Nereis diversicolor is most abundant in that part of an estuary where maximal amplitude and rate of change of salinity take place, though it may be found in water which is practically fresh and in salt-marsh pools in which the salt content is higher than that of ocean water. Presumably its abundance in the middle reaches of an estuary is due to absence of competition with other species unable to withstand such conditions. But it is not only tolerant of a wide range of salt concentrations, it is also able to regulate its weight and the salt content of the coelomic fluid in diluted sea water.

If a *Nereis diversicolor* is placed in diluted sea water, its weight at first increases rapidly by osmotic inflow; during this period Beadle[8] found an enhanced oxygen uptake which was reduced after an hour when in this particular experiment the weight began to decline. Beadle ascribed this to resistance to swelling. Many other species (such as *Perinereis cultrifera*) cannot do this; their weight continues to increase and they eventually die. Some (such as *Nereis virens*) have a more limited ability than *N. diversicolor* to regulate their weights, that is, they can do so only in more moderate dilutions. Beadle[7] showed that if water from which oxygen had been removed, or to which small amounts of potassium cyanide were added, was used, *N. diversicolor* behaved like *P. cultrifera*, and the mechanism of weight regulation was clearly disabled in some way. Beadle[8] also showed that weight regulation broke down if the diluted sea water (20%) lacked calcium ions. Furthermore, if worms were transferred from 20% sea water in which they had already regulated their weight to 20% sea water in which calcium ions were lacking, the weight increased. It is suggested that calcium ions decrease the permeability of the epidermis to water, and that this consequently allows a greater inflow of water than can be removed by the nephridia so that the weight increases. Jørgensen and I[92] maintained that the ability of *N. diversicolor* to withstand such drastic dilution as it does may well be due to the skin having a lower permeability to water than species such as *N. virens* or *N. pelagica*. We postulated that *N. diversicolor* showed reduced permeability to salt in low concentrations, but Potts and Parry[127] have re-interpreted the data, and concluded that it is not necessary to make this deduction.

Over a wide range of salinities the chloride content of the body fluids of *Nereis diversicolor* follows passively that of the medium. In worms that have attained equilibrium there is a certain critical value (about 8 g Cl/l) below which the osmotic pressure of the coelomic fluid is maintained above that of the medium. This implies an ability for active salt uptake against the osmotic gradient. This was shown by Beadle[7] and Ellis,[53] and confirmed by Jørgensen and myself[92] using the radio-isotope ^{36}Cl and Fretter[60] using ^{24}Na. Fretter demonstrated that in normal sea water there was an uptake of 240–75μg Na/g/hr; in 50% sea water an uptake of 60μg/g/hr, and in 25% sea water (9%) 180μg/g/hr. Her results also demonstrated that in 25% sea water the rate of uptake of sodium ions was attained when the weight of the animal reached its maximum value, and was maintained during the period when the weight was being reduced, emphasizing the separate regulation of water and of ions.

The ecological problems involved in penetration of brackish waters and areas of very low salinity have received much attention from Smith.[144] The ability to withstand lowered salinities in the laboratory may partly be governed by the sort of conditions encountered in the habitat from which the animals were collected. Smith found that *Nereis diversicolor* from Finland and from the east coast of England were equally able to adjust their volume and to osmoregulate when subjected to diluted media, after adaptation to ocean water. Temperature appears to play an important part in the lowest salinities at which the species can occur. Smith found the apparently anomalous situation that this species does not occur in as low salinites in Finland as in Denmark or England. The closely related and possibly synonymous *N. limnicola*, on the other hand, lives in the freshwater Lake Merced, California, as well as in estuaries in the same region, and Smith[145] has found that those from Lake Merced have the same or slightly higher body-fluid chloride content than their estuarine relatives, and can regulate their weights slightly more effectively when replaced in diluted sea water after adaptation to more saline water. Whilst the weights of those from Lake Merced do not rise as much as those from estuaries, the initial rate of increase is much the same, suggesting that they are possibly better able to produce an increased flow of urine. Ellis, on the other hand, maintained that *Nereis diversicolor* from Roscoff regulated their weights better than those from Bangor.[53] The part which the nephridia play in the regulation of both water and ions in nereids deserves further study. Krishnan has found in the freshwater *Lycastis indica* that the nephridia are not only larger than in either estuarine or marine species, but that they have a greatly improved vascular supply.[92]

Much remains to be done before we fully understand the mechanisms involved in these processes. The varying salinity which occurs in estuaries by mixing of fresh water and sea water by tidal variation has posed physiological problems of importance particularly to annelids living, as so many do, in the muds deposited under such conditions. In view of the lack of evidence that the nephridia do more than act as drains as far as nitrogenous wastes are concerned, we can but incline to the view that they are primarily osmoregulators.

6

THE NERVOUS SYSTEM AND THE CO-ORDINATION OF MOVEMENT

THE need for nervous co-ordination of a muscular system, built up from a series of segmental units into a body functioning as a whole, may best be met by a longitudinal nerve cord or cords passing from one end to the other and from which lateral nerves arise in each segment. A longitudinal cord may be found in a ventral position in annelids lying against the body wall underneath the gut. The cord may be a single strand or may be double, the two strands being bound together, but more rarely lying wide apart. The amphinomids are peculiar in having four longitudinal cords. Storch[149] thought that this tetraneurous condition was primitive, and that the parapodial ganglia of other worms represented all that remained of these more lateral cords. Lateral cords are found also in other annelids such as *Nereis*, but they do not appear to be equivalent to those of amphinomids.

The ventral nerve cord bifurcates anterior to a ventral ganglion, usually termed the suboesophageal ganglion, although it rarely lies under the oesophagus. Each commissure passes the stomodeum to a median dorsal brain, which may also be referred to as the cerebral ganglia, suprapharyngeal or supraoesophageal ganglia. The ventral ganglion will be referred to here as the suboesophageal ganglion and the dorsal ganglia as the brain. The brain is a bilaterally symmetrical lobed mass receiving nerves from the sensory structures of the prostomium: the palps, antennae, eyes and nuchal organs. In actively motile worms such as *Nereis* or *Eunice*, in which such sense organs are well developed, the brain is relatively large and fills the prostomium. In burrowers like the lugworm, and in tubicolous worms such as the sabellids, the brain is much smaller. The prostomial origin of the brain was discussed in chapter 1, but it may be recalled that in adult earthworms and leeches the brain comes to lie farther back within the anterior segments.

The nerves arising from the ventral nerve cord in each segment are paired, supplying the muscles of the body wall and gut. Paired segmental nerves also receive fibres from a subepidermal plexus related to peripheral sense organs and from proprioceptors within the muscles. The gut may also receive an additional nerve supply from the circumoesophageal commissures. The nerve cord varies in thickness, being dilated into ganglia at intervals throughout its length, one ganglion corresponding to each segment though sometimes intersegmental in position. It is from these ganglia that the paired lateral nerves arise, and it is only there that a cortex containing the bodies of the nerve cells is to be found. The nerve cord of most annelids appears to be circular or rather horizontally flattened in transverse section and to consist of a mass of mainly longitudinally directed fibres surrounded by a fibrous sheath. Within this mass of fibres one or more may be found to be very much larger than the others: these are the giant fibres which arise from specially large nerve cells. Most annelids have them, but they are lacking in some polychaetes such as syllids and phyllodocids.

The giant-fibre system

Giant fibres have been known for some time, but their nervous nature was not at first appreciated. Bovard found that after transection of the nerve cord in the earthworm ordinary locomotory movements were resumed before quick end-to-end contractions, and it was then realized that this was correlated with the slower regeneration of the giant fibres. Prosser also found that end-to-end contractions were the last of the movements to appear in the growing earthworm larva, and that this ability was correlated with the appearance of the giant fibres. We now know quite a lot about these large nerves and how they work.[117] In general they enable impulses to travel rapidly from one end of the body to the other, so that the longitudinal muscles of every segment supplied can contract almost simultaneously. The value of such a system is evident when one considers the elongate nature of annelid bodies, and is especially important to tubicolous worms whose only escape reaction can be a rapid withdrawal into the tube. By far the largest giant fibres are indeed found in sabellids; in *Myxicola* there is a single giant fibre which may be as much as 1·5 mm in diameter, by far the largest nerve fibre known.

There are two kinds of giant fibre in annelids: one consists of a single long axon formed from a single large nerve cell; the other is a syncytial fibre contributed by a number of cells (fig. 14). Both types occur in the same animal. In the scaleworm, *Euthalenessa*, for example, there is a pair of large cells in each ganglion whose fibres cross and pass out contra-laterally into a segmental nerve (fig. 14A). In addition, other large cells have their axons directed longitudinally. Six of these lie in the suboesophageal ganglion, their fibres passing backward, two pairs decussating and one pair sending their axons down the other side. Another pair of fibres apparently arises in the brain or in the circumoesophageal commissures, and a further median fibre is contributed by two cells certainly lying in the brain. In addition to these giant fibres contributed by cells at the anterior end of the body, others lying in the posterior ganglia have axons passing forward. Complicated as this system seems, there are additional longitudinal fibres of smaller size with lateral connexions to the paired segmental nerves. These convey impulses more slowly than the giant fibres, and are presumably related to the ordinary muscular activities of the body.

The arrangement of the giant fibres in *Euthalenessa* is only one example of many in which a system of enlarged single neurons has been evolved for rapid through-

conduction of impulses. In eunicidans the arrangement also
consists entirely of single giant neurons, as far as is known.
In *Halla parthenopeia* there is a series of cells lying anteriorly with their axons directed posteriorly, and a similar
series of posteriorly situated cell bodies with their axons
passing forwards (figs. 14B, 14C). In *Eunice* and *Marphysa*

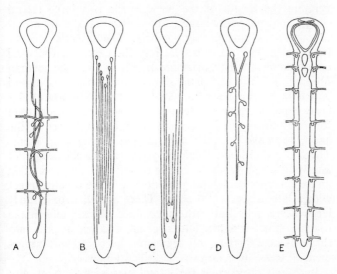

FIG. 14. Giant fibre patterns in polychaetes: A, *Euthalenessa
dendrolepis*; B, C, *Halla parthenopeia*; D, *Clymene producta*;
E, *Myxicola infundibulum*. Redrawn after Nicol[117]

there is apparently only one enormous giant fibre passing
from one end of the nerve cord to the other, while they are
absent altogether in some arabellids. The largest simple
giant axons of this type are those of *Eunice* which are 100μ
across in a large worm. They are commonly much less than
this, however, 20μ perhaps being nearer the average
diameter. The diameter varies with the state of contraction
of the worm, and axons will appear larger in a section of a
worm which contracted when fixed. Such distortion of the

fibres undoubtedly occurs under natural conditions, and implies a fair elasticity of the axon.

In other polychaetes, and in the oligochaetes, some giant fibres are syncytial conducting threads which receive contributions from a number of neurons. All the nereids, for example, have giant fibres of this type as well as unicellular giant fibres.[142] In *Nereis* there are five giant fibres running the length of the nerve cord: two large lateral fibres, and one fairly large median fibre flanked by a pair of somewhat smaller paramedials. The laterals are the largest and their fibres extend into the circumoesophageal commissures as they originate in the brain. The median fibre is related to one or more neurons in the oesophageal ganglion. The smaller paramedial fibres are of the unicellular type, a pair of cells in each segment sending a short fibre forwards through two segments to the distal part of the axon, to make a touch contact with the one in front. There is an additional pair of giant cells in each segment anastomosing by a short fibre in the mid-line, each sending an axon across the lateral giant fibre to make touch contact with a lateral segmental nerve. There are also some fairly large nerve cells but with much finer fibres which make touch contact with the lateral giants and which pass into the ipsi- or contra-lateral segmental nerves. The arrangement of these finer fibres is described below.

In *Nereis diversicolor* the lateral giants are about 40μ across, the median 34μ, the paramedials 13μ;[117] the laterals are related to the main longitudinal muscles, the median to the anterior oblique muscles, and the paramedials to the posterior oblique muscles of the parapodia.[87]

Syncytial giant fibres are commonly interconnected. In *Arenicola marina*, for example, there are, as in *Nereis*, three main longitudinal fibres: a lateral pair and one median fibre. All anastomose with one another and are joined by a pair of large nerve cells, or sometimes by only a single nerve cell, in each segment. Lateral connexions passing out through the segmental nerves here arise directly from the lateral giants. There are many variations in such interconnecting systems. In *Sabella*, where the nerve cord is double, a single giant fibre passes down each half of the cord and anastomoses with the fibre of the other half in each of the ladder-like cross connexions. In *Myxicola* the cord is undivided and the two lateral giants, while separate (though cross-connected) in the first two segments, fuse to form a single enormous giant axon (fig. 14E). In addition large fibres pass out directly from the longitudinal fibre into the segmental nerves; even the lateral branches may be as much as 85μ in diameter and each is related near its origin to a giant cell.

Large as these fibres are, none of the nerve fibres of polychaetes seem to have a fatty sheath comparable with the myelinated fibres of vertebrates. In earthworms, however, the giant fibres do have fatty sheaths though the proportion of sheath to axon is relatively small. They are essentially like frog sciatic nerve fibres, in ultrastructure and in the radial arrangement of the lipid and tangentially oriented protein molecules. Each of the three giant axons of *Lumbricus terrestris* is divided in each segment by cross-partitions or 'macrosynapses' as in the lateral giants of *Nereis*. The function of these oblique synapses is puzzling; they are essentially elliptical discs of myelin and appear to be histological rather than physiological boundaries. Little is known about the development of giant fibres and of the origin of these synapses. The two lateral fibres communicate segmentally by ring-like anastomoses, but they do not connect with the median fibre.

Before turning to the way in which these fibres work, it is interesting to note the occurrence of this system. In short-bodied scuttling worms such as *Aphrodite* or *Hermione*, it is absent; in nereids there is a mixed system of simple uni-cellular fibres of limited extent and syncytial fibres running from one end to the other, and finally in the fanworms the fibres are large, syncytial and inter-connected. Giant fibres may also be lost; there are none in *Chaetopterus* though they are present in the spionids from which they are certainly derived. Giant fibres are absent in leeches.

There is no doubt that the giant-fibre system has been evolved for the rapid conduction of impulses enabling almost simultaneous stimulation of all the longitudinal muscles with consequent overall contraction. It is doubtful if they participate in the relay of other impulses. In *Myxicola*, Nicol[117] was able to sever the giant axon without interrupting the rest of the nerve cord and only these end-to-end body jerks were obliterated. The speed of conduction in these giant fibres is much greater than in the finer fibres of the nerve cord. When a shadow passes over the crown, or if a pebble is thrown into the water nearby, most sabellids and serpulids promptly retract within the tube with startling rapidity.

Impulses in these giant axons may be distinguished from those in the finer fibres by their much larger action potentials, for when an impulse passes two suitably placed electrodes in the nerve cord, the potential difference across the sheath is larger the greater the diameter of the axon. In cords with several giants of different size each may be identified by the different height of the action potential, and by recording the passage of impulses caused by stimulating different parts of the body it is possible to determine the direction in which impulses are conveyed and the speed of their transmission. Such physiological mapping has been done by Bullock[20] and Rushton.[136] Bullock found that in *Nereis* each giant may conduct in either direction independently of the other fibres, and that the laterals may be stimulated at all levels. The median fibre, on the other hand, is fired only by anterior stimulation, and the paramedials only by stimulation towards the posterior end. While conduction can take place in either direction, it is normally in one direction or the other owing to the sensory connexions. Rushton independently came to the same conclusions with regard to *Lumbricus*. In the sabellid *Eudistylia polymorpha* there is 'cross-talk' between the two longitudinal fibres, for when the fibre on one side alone is stimulated a return impulse may be found in the other, the transmission occurring in the cross-connexions which act as non-polarized two-way synapses, and also where the fibres decussate in the sub-oesophageal ganglion.

The larger the diameter of the axon the greater the speed of conduction. The conduction velocities in the giant fibres of *Nereis virens* were first measured by Bullock.[20] The laterals are the largest and carry the fastest impulses (6·2 m/s); in the rather smaller medians they travel at 5·4 m/s, and in the smallest paramedials at only 2·5/s. Nicol[117] has recorded a velocity of 20 m/s in fibres 0·1–1·0 mm diameter in *Myxicola*, and also established that, in this fibre at least, the conduction velocity was proportional to the square-root of the diameter. The same relationship has been found in the giant axon of cephalopods. On the other hand, conduction velocity was not affected in *Lumbricus* and *Eudistylia* when the axons were stretched, thereby reducing their diameter. The median fibre of *Lumbricus terrestris*, while only 90–160μ in diameter, has a conduction velocity of 20–45 m/s, greater than that of *Myxicola* even though the diameter is less, and this is almost certainly due to the myelinated sheath. Rushton[136] found the median giant to conduct at 20 m/s, the laterals at 10 m/s. The earthworm's lateral giant has a sheath diameter equal to 10% of that of the whole fibre; that of *Myxicola* is only 1%. A cat's saphenous nerve fibre, on the other hand, has a sheath 24% of the total diameter, and much higher conduction velocities are achieved, although only 7μ across. It is curious that the fanworms have not evolved this system, though much smaller fibres in spionids, maldanids and capitellids, as well as in earthworms, are at least to some extent myelinated.

The large size of the giant fibre of *Myxicola* lends itself to physiological study, and Nicol's work has added much to our knowledge of how giant fibres function. As there is only a single giant fibre occupying almost the whole of the nerve cord, one can be reasonably sure, by using too small an amplification to pick up the action potentials of the smaller fibres, that the spikes recorded are indeed related to the giant axon. Not only have the speed and direction of conduction been recorded by placing electrodes at intervals along the cord, but it has also been found that conduction is an all-or-nothing affair and that increasing the stimulus has no effect on the action potential.[122] It was also found that the fibre conducts equally well in either direction and may successfully be fired at any level of the body, unlike the fibres of *Nereis* or *Lumbricus* which normally conduct in one direction or another, not because of any physiological polarization, but because of their afferent connexions, as Bullock and Rushton have shown. The *Myxicola* fibre enables all the longitudinal muscles to contract synergically within a much shorter time after a sufficient stimulus is received at any part of the body than if other fibre tracts were utilized. The reduction of these in *Myxicola* is a reflection of its tubicolous existence and the relative simplicity or standardization of its other muscular movements. Nicol and Whitteridge[122] have calculated that it takes 10 msec for an impulse to travel from one end of the body to the other in a 12 cm *Myxicola*. In other annelids the speed of conduction in the ordinary fibre tracts is about 0·5 m/s (as compared with 12 m/s in the *Myxicola* giant fibre) and would take 240 msec to travel this length. As it takes about 260 msec for the muscles to develop their maximum twitch, the giant fibre may be said to halve the total reaction time.

Myxicola seems to be more advanced than other polychaetes in that the efferent giant-fibre connexions give rise directly to branches which subdivide into the longitudinal muscles. In other polychaetes that are sufficiently known the giant-fibre impulses are relayed by specially large neurons whose axons make touch contacts with the giant axon. Horridge[87] has directed attention to this relay system in *Nereis*, and in the scaleworm *Harmothoë*; and his results are particularly interesting in relation to a characteristic feature of giant-fibre response that we have yet to mention: their rapid habituation. Nicol[119] found that after a couple of fast responses to shadow in the sabellid, *Branchiomma*, further stimulation was ignored. *Myxicola* when first picked up will twitch violently, but after several twitches the worm will lie motionless in the hand. Horridge[87] noticed that in

Nereis, when the lateral fibres were stimulated at frequencies of less than 1/s, the longitudinal muscles gave a single twitch in response to each stimulus, but that this response soon fails, although the impulses in the giant fibres remain. Clearly the failure to respond is not due to failure of the giant fibre itself, but to the relay or to the neuromuscular junction. That it is the relay (afferent or efferent) which is responsible is indicated by return of the response after failure following repeated stimulation of one set of giant fibres, by stimulation of another. The failure is not, therefore, due to muscular fatigue or failure of the sensory cells to fire. In *Nereis* if the anal cirri are stimulated the whole body shortens, but if the stimulus is repeated a different response is elicited, the tail being moved slowly to one side. This second response, unlike the end-to-end twitch, may be repeatedly evoked.

The nerve cord of Nereis

Before describing the connexions of these giant relay neurons it may be as well to look at the arrangement of fine-fibre tracts in the nerve cord. These are best known in *Nereis* from the studies of Smith.[142] There are six longitudinal fine-fibre tracts (fig. 15). In each segment the cord is dilated into a ganglion which occupies perhaps two-thirds of the length of each segment, and from which four pairs of nerves arise. Of these the second (II) and fourth (IV) are largest. The cell bodies are contained in a cortex lying ventrally and laterally to the main mass of axons. Cells supplying these longitudinal tracts are unipolar, their axons rising through or crossing the neuropile. The cells either run from one axon to the next where touch contact is made with the proximal part of the next axon; or the axon is T-shaped, the cell body lying ventrally or ventro-laterally at the bottom of the T and the tips of the arms synapsing with those of the next neuron. All the segmental nerves are mixed, carrying motor impulses out from the cord, and conveying sensory impulses inward; though there are more motor axons in nerves II and IV. The sensory fibres connect with one or other of the longitudinal tracts on the same side. The sensory fibres entering from nerves I and II are mostly related to the latero-dorsal tract; those from nerves III and IV to the medio-dorsal. I and IV contain afferent fibres stimulated by sense cells in the skin, II from the parapodia and especially from the parapodial cirri; III carries mainly fibres from proprioceptors. There seems to be no direct connexion between the afferent (sensory) fibres and the giant fibres, though it is probable that those entering from II and IV to the ventral fine longitudinal tract may connect with the main (lateral) giants through the fine network of internunciary neurons. Nerves II and IV carry the main afferent sensory fibres from the integument and parapodia —areas most likely to receive stimuli of an emergency kind. It is interesting that these relate most closely with the largest (lateral) giant fibres, and that there is some evidence that their connexions, even via an internuncial network of fibres, are closer than with the other fibres. That this is likely is also suggested by the lower threshold of the lateral giants.[142]

The main motor axons cross through the dorsal part of the neuropile from the contra-lateral side before entering the segmental nerve, enabling a maximum number of contacts to be made with the internuncial fibres rising from the ventral cortex to the dorsal side and crossing the upper part of the neuropile. It is these large contra-laterally sited motor neurons which also make contact with the lateral and median giant fibres.[87] This may be done by the motor axon curling round the giant fibre, by just touching it, or less often by collateral dendrites.

The number of neurons in each ganglion is relatively small, but their complex interconnexions make up for their apparent simplicity. The arrangement of these fine-fibre tracts is presumably adapted for transmission of the impulses required for ordinary muscular and locomotory activities of the body, which are co-ordinated from one segment to the next by the longitudinal fine-fibre tracts. The giant fibres, specialized as they are for rapid responses, thus

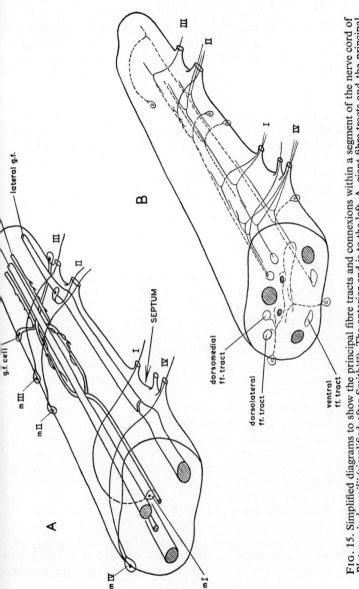

FIG. 15. Simplified diagrams to show the principal fibre tracts and connexions within a segment of the nerve cord of *Platynereis dumerilii* (simplified after Smith[142]). The anterior end is to the left. A, giant-fibre tracts and the principal motor neurons (mI-IV) of the segmental nerves (mI-IV) on the left-hand side; B, showing the principal sensory fibres (continuous lines) and fine-fibre tracts, together with the main types of internunciary neurons (broken lines)

lateral g.f.

g.f. cell

III

II

mIII

mII

I

IV

mIV

mI

SEPTUM

A

B

III

II

I

IV

dorsomedial ff. tract

dorsolateral ff. tract

ventral ff. tract

stimulate the muscles by the same motor axons, so that an emergency impulse has the effect of immediately cancelling any ordinary sequence of movement which may have been in progress. These motor neurons do not themselves inner-vate the muscles, the axon terminating against other axons, or making dendritic synapses with at least one other motor neuron lying more peripherally against the muscle block. The motor neurons of the second or third order also synapse with receptors in the integument nearby, so that local responses should be possible without the intervention of the nerve cord. Wilson[170] has confirmed Smith's findings with nerve-muscle preparations and by stimulating individual fibres in each of the four segmental nerves of *Nereis* with microelectrodes. He has also found that the cell bodies in the parapodial ganglion are not simply relay neurons, but probably integrate motor reflex circuits within a single parapodium.

The giant-fibre system may thus be likened to a fast motorway which bypasses all main points and which may only be reached or left by minor links. None of the giant fibres is connected directly to any sensory system and it is only fired by impulses greater than those carried by the fine-fibre circuits which presumably co-ordinate normal mus-cular activity. Wilson[170] has confirmed that there are two kinds of response in the segmental nerves of *Nereis*: a fast response, large at the first shock and fatiguing quickly (giant fibre and nerve IV), and a slow response which is small at first but shows facilitation above a stimulation frequency of 10/s. That the giant-fibre system is not an integral part of the co-ordinating mechanism of locomotory movement is suggested by the fact that syllids and phyllodocids which crawl and swim in a manner essentially like that of *Nereis* have none.

Drug action

Before considering the patterns of muscular activity in different annelids, it will perhaps not be out of place to mention here that the muscles involved in such movements are cholinergic, that is, they go into tonic contraction under the influence of acetylcholine, and are sensitized by eserine. There is considerable variation, however, in the responses of annelid muscles to drugs, and it would be unwise to generalize.

Evidence for an antagonistic system of adrenergic and cholinergic nerves supplying the gut in the earthworm, very reminiscent of the system in vertebrates, has been found by Wu[175] and Millott.[111] The gut, as noted in an earlier chapter, has a double nerve supply. Wu found those from the circumoesophageal commissures to be exciting and cholinergic, and those farther back to be inhibiting and adrenergic. He found further that these reactions of the gut to drugs are rather like those of the body wall, which is somewhat insensitive to acetylcholine alone, though sensitized by eserine. Prosser[130] found evidence that annelid hearts and dorsal vessels are neurogenic, being affected by acetylcholine as in most arthropods, and unlike those of molluscs and vertebrates. The contractile sinuses of *Hirudo*, on the other hand, are myogenic, and these also have a system of accelerator and depressor nerves.

The locomotion of Nereis *and* Nephthys

The co-ordination of locomotion in animals including that of annelids has been studied intensely by Sir James Gray and his colleagues at Cambridge.

The locomotory movements of *Nereis diversicolor* are effected by two distinct mechanisms which amplify each other, and are produced by the action of the longitudinal muscles, and by the muscles of the parapodia.[69] In either case each side of the segment is out of phase with the other; when the longitudinal muscles on one side are contracted, those on the other are relaxed; when one parapodium is directed forward, the other is directed back. When a nereid starts to crawl it appears as if all the parapodia from one end of the body to the other begin their stepping almost simultaneously, the body being thrown into slight lateral waves which travel forward. Cinematograph film has shown that this forward propagation of the stepping wave is established by a very rapid wave which passes down the body from the head, indicated by every fourth to eighth parapodium making a forward step. The forward-travelling wave is then established by each parapodium in front of these initially stepping parapodia moving forward. During slow crawling it is the parapodia which propel the body, though the propulsive force is imparted during the effective backward stroke by the contraction of the ipsi-lateral longitudinal muscles as well as the posterior parapodial muscles. As they do so the aciculum and chaetae are protruded to grip the ground. Each segment moves forward when the longitudinal muscles relax and when the parapodium swings forward and slightly upward by contraction of the anterior parapodial muscles with the aciculum and chaetae retracted. A wave of contraction in the longitudinal muscles passes forward on each side, out of phase with the muscles of the other side, so that the body is thrown into lateral undulations. As the amplitude of these waves increases the worm rises from the surface and swims. The waves still travel forward and the parapodia still perform the same strokes, but they then act as paddles preventing the worm from moving backwards. Such swimming looks inefficient, the worms apparently exerting a great deal of energy without swimming fast or far; most soon sink down to the bottom and start crawling. In heteronereids the parapodia are greatly increased in surface area and musculature and they can swim much faster and for longer periods than unmetamorphosed worms. The muscles of the body wall are partly histolysed and those of the parapodia augmented in these swimming nereids.

Parapodia are clearly also important in the locomotion of *Nephthys* which is a much better swimmer than *Nereis*. This greater efficiency seems partly to be due to the more definitive parapodial stroke which is given more rapidly and most effectively on the crest of the lateral undulatory wave, as Clark and Clark[27] have clearly demonstrated. The effective parapodial stroke occupies a much smaller proportion of the total locomotory cycle of each segment than in *Nereis*, and as the speed of swimming is increased the number of waves into which the body is thrown is also increased with a consequent decrease in the ratio of wavelength to amplitude. The resting phase of the parapodial stroke is then almost abolished so that the parapodia effectively execute continuous paddling movements. The increase in frequency with the increase of speed is the opposite of what occurs in *Nereis*. The nervous co-ordination of locomotion in *Nephthys* has not been worked out, but in view of the greater importance of the parapodial muscles it may be rather different from that of *Nereis*.

We also know little about how locomotory activities of *Nereis* may be related to the neural pathways. The fact that well-co-ordinated swimming movements may be maintained after removal of the head or brain, by transection of the nerve cord, or by an isolated part of the body, suggests that the locomotory rhythm in the normal animal, once established, can be maintained by local peripheral circuits.

During both crawling and swimming, the activity of the muscles of the two sides of a segment is out of phase, but this is not so when a nereid is irrigating the burrow. If a worm is confined in a piece of glass tubing of suitable bore, the body is thrown into undulatory waves in the vertical plane by the muscles on both sides working together, the waves passing back from the head. When once initiated the wave may be stopped by stimulation at either end of the body, the whole wave may be obliterated, or the worm may stop, leaving the body thrown into a series of standing waves. In either case the activity can be resumed, the old wave being obliterated by a new one.

Locomotion of the earthworm

Simultaneous contraction of the longitudinal muscles of both sides of a segment and a wave passing backward from the head occurs also when an earthworm crawls on

a rough horizontal surface.[70] Forward progression actually
begins by a wave of contraction in the circular muscles
passing back from the head. When this wave has reached
the middle of the body, a wave of contraction in the longitudinal muscles starts at the anterior end and passes backwards, to be followed by another wave of contraction of the
circular muscles, and so on. Each segment moves forward
when the longitudinal muscles relax and its forward progression slows down and ceases as they contract. The
segments moving forward are lifted slightly to reduce
frictional resistance. The chaetae are protruded and withdrawn in a similar cycle, so that they are thrust out to make
contact with the ground when the segment forms a temporary 'foot' against which the muscles of neighbouring
segments can act. Those immediately in front push against
it in extending forward (the longitudinals relaxing, the
circulars contracting), and those behind exert a pull equal
to the frictional resistance of the more posterior segments
which are moving forward over the ground. It would appear
that the mouth is also used as a sucker, the segments being
pulled after, much as in a leech, and that this is the way
earthworms can crawl out from a glass tank with clean
vertical sides.

It has been mentioned that in *Nereis* small sections of
the body attempt to crawl in a normal fashion. In the
earthworm this is only true if the ventral surface of the body
is in contact with the substratum, or if some artificial
stimulus is applied. If a decapitated earthworm is suspended
in air, the body exhibits a normal cycle of locomotory
movement. If the stretch caused by its own weight be reduced by immersion in water, the activity disappears, but
it promptly returns when pulled out. The same thing
happens when a normal worm crawling over a rough surface
is lifted up by a series of threads previously looped under
the body. Either a background of peripheral stimulation is
necessary for maintaining the rhythm, or the stretch caused
in one muscle block by contraction in the neighbouring
segment against the temporary 'foot' is an essential part of

the mechanism. However this may be, such peripheral tactile reflexes could not initiate locomotory movements. It could be that such peripheral reflexes are more important in some circumstances than others, or are to be regarded as an additional method for co-ordinating the movements of the whole body; if a worm be cut almost in two, so that the two parts are joined only by the nerve cord, their movements are still co-ordinated. Of course, the nerve cord might be acting purely mechanically.

It is of some interest, therefore, to know whether the nerve cord possesses any inherent electrical rhythms coinciding with the rhythms shown by the muscles. This has, in fact, been demonstrated.[70] If an incision is made in the body wall, the nerve cord exposed, and the segmental nerves cut throughout a short length of the body which may then be used to secure the worm, electrical activity in the nerve cord may be picked up by electrodes only when the remainder of the body wall is active. Furthermore, the bursts of electrical activity in the nerve cord coincide with the locomotory movements. Nothing appears to happen when the body is quiescent. While a completely isolated nerve cord also shows prolonged activity, this does not seem to be rhythmic and implies that the peripheral impulses do play a part in the maintenance of the series of reflexes causing the locomotory cycle.

The earthworm can reverse the direction of its locomotory movements, waves of contraction passing forward. Both forward and backward waves can be stopped by a sudden stimulus. When activity starts again, the sequence may be continued from where it left off, the arrested wave passing on. In other instances, a new wave starts and obliterates the old when it passes; or it may be obliterated by another wave initiated at the opposite end. This indicates a fairly complex central nerve cord connexion, more central perhaps than the circuits of *Nereis*. Collier[30] found evidence for the conduction of these different patterns by separate fine-fibre tracts, for after transection of the cord different times were required for each to be re-established. There is no evidence that each ganglion is a reflex centre for the antagonistic contraction of the longitudinal and circular muscles of that segment, but neurons connecting it with adjacent ganglia co-ordinate these movements with those of neighbouring segments. As in *Nereis* there are several pairs of segmental nerves (three in *Lumbricus terrestris*) which are mixed, with axons passing ipsi- and contra-laterally.

Whilst every segment is a unit, therefore, each is closely co-ordinated with those adjacent to it and with the whole body. In this connexion it is interesting that Prosser[129] found that in *Lumbricus terrestris* the sensory fibres in each of the segmental nerves could be stimulated from the epidermis not only of the same segment but of that in front and of that behind, each pair of nerves receiving stimuli from a clearly defined epidermal field.

From the observations of the nervous control of locomotion in earthworms an interesting question arises: are the rhythmic muscular activities we have been describing actuated by an inherent rhythmicity of the nerve cord, which may, nevertheless, be modified or halted by peripheral stimuli, or is the rhythm determined by a sequence of peripheral reflexes which may be merely initiated or obliterated by over-riding impulses in the nerve cord? In this regard, the maintenance of the locomotory sequence in leeches is of especial interest.

Locomotion of the leech

A leech can move about in two distinct ways. When swimming the body is thrown into undulations in the dorso-ventral plane, the waves passing backward from the head. When moving over the substratum, amongst plants, or over the body of a host, the leech loops along by alternately attaching and releasing the suckers at each end of the body. The longitudinal and circular muscles are involved in both types of movement.

When the animal is attached by the posterior sucker, motion starts by a wave of contraction in the circular muscles passing back from the head so that the body extends forward. The anterior sucker is then attached, the posterior released, and a similar wave of contraction of the longitudinals pulls the body forward. This form of progression, therefore, consists of a series of steps, the two suckers being alternately applied and released, the attachment of one causing the release of the other. Gray, Lissman and Pumphrey[71] found that if a leech is suspended by a thread, and one sucker is presented with a microscope cover-slip which it will grip, this will be dropped when the other sucker attaches itself to another cover-slip. A wave of contraction in the circulars on attachment of the posterior sucker, and in the longitudinals on attachment of the anterior sucker, is also invariably produced. When the animal swims there is no peripheral stimulation and there is no such rhythm. It might be concluded that these stepping movements depend on the suckers, but this is not so, for the suckers may be removed or denervated without abolishing the muscular rhythm, provided that the ventral surface of the body is stimulated. Gray and his collaborators concluded that the suckers were acting as time signals for each phase of the movement, and are the normal, but not essential, channels for peripheral excitation. There seems to be no inherent rhythm in the nerve cord, and the sequence of movements is dependent on peripheral reflexes normally associated with the suckers.

Fixation of the posterior sucker actually inhibits contraction of the longitudinal muscles. If a leech is decapitated, or the suboesophageal ganglion is severed, the circular muscles lose their ability to contract, but the posterior sucker does not lose its ability to attach. When this occurs the longitudinals start relaxing. Not only is the rhythm, once established, dependent on these peripheral reflexes, but very likely also on proprioceptors in the muscles themselves, and these may well play a dominating role when the body is either impeded or stretched. The frequency of the rhythm is determined by the time it takes the longitudinal muscles to undergo complete isotonic contraction: the rate may be slowed down by weighting the animal.

E

As in the earthworm, the locomotory rhythm of *Hirudo* is carried by the nerve cord and is not interrupted by denervating several segments part way down the body, though removal of the suboesophageal ganglion does effectively obliterate the rhythm. Swimming occurs when all peripheral stimulation is removed, as happens, for example, when a leech is dropped into water, and continues until the anterior sucker is attached to some object. Swimming then ceases abruptly, and may be succeeded by the stepping just described. Decapitation or removal of the suboesophageal ganglion has no effect on swimming, as might be expected, for such anterior severance of the nerve cord has the effect of removing any possibility of stimuli passing down the cord. Swimming may then be stopped by a gentle touch on the underside of the body, but the movements may start again spontaneously when the stimulus is removed. Touching the dorsal side has no effect. In other words, swimming movements can only manifest themselves in the absence of tactile stimulation; stepping only in their presence.

A certain amount of peripheral stimulation is also necessary to maintain an electrical rhythm in the nerve cord of the leech. This is shown by removal of the suboesophageal ganglion and exposure of the cord over about ten segments, the nerves in this region being severed save for one nerve which is attached to a recording apparatus. The muscles of the severed part may be used to anchor the preparation so that the posterior undamaged end hangs freely in water. It is then found that when the hind end shows swimming movements a well-defined electrical rhythm is picked up in the tapped nerve, and the rhythm is lost when the cord is cut just in front of the swimming region. Only arhythmic activity can be observed if the ganglia of the intact part of the cord are subsequently touched. That the local proprioceptive activity is not restricted to the segment in which it occurs shows that the nerve cord, when sufficiently excited, co-ordinates the movements of the whole body in a rhythmic manner.

Collier[30] has shown this also in *Lumbricus terrestris*. He found that either tactile stimulation or stretching initiated the rhythm in a short, ligatured piece of worm containing the nerve cord, but that the rhythm soon disappeared in the absence of repeated stimulation. The nerve cord is necessary for perpetuation of the rhythm, for while its excision does not abolish contraction of the muscles when stimulated, it does abolish any regularity such contractions would otherwise have. Collier concluded that the rhythmicity of movement follows a regular variation in the level of excitability created at some point in the reflex arc by the stream of impulses from the peripheral (tactile or proprioceptive) sense organs.

We can now answer our question by saying that such rhythms are not initiated by the nerve cord, but that the cord is nevertheless capable of translating a stream of impulses arising in peripheral sense organs into a rhythmic alternation of excitation of two muscle sets, the circular and the longitudinal. As Collier points out, it is very like the scratching reflex of the dog when the flank is given a prolonged pinch.

Other movements

Not all movements involving rhythmic co-ordination of the longitudinal and circular muscles of the whole body are, of course, locomotory. Wells and his colleagues have demonstrated that *Arenicola marina* shows several activities which often alternate with remarkable regularity. Unlike the results obtained with the experiments on the nerve cord of the leech and earthworm just described, it has been shown that these activities are related either to spontaneous rhythms in the nerve cord or to initiation by the nervous system of the oesophagus acting as a kind of alarm clock or pacemaker. If an *Arenicola* is pinned down in a dish under sea water which is kept aerated and stirred in an unvaried manner, the movements of the worm may be recorded on a smoked drum by a lever attached to a thread hooked into the body wall. Such preparations show regular bursts of activity for long periods even though no stimuli are applied. Strips of body wall containing the nerve cord show the same timing of activity which exactly resembles the irrigation-defaecation cycle of normal worms described in chapter 3. The oesophagus shows a similar rhythmic activity with the same timing as the feeding cycle, and it continues to do so even when cut into strips. Whitear[169] has shown that the nervous system in the wall of the oesophagus forms a diffuse net so that there is presumably enough of this left even in a strip to act as a physiological clock. It seems unlikely that the clock works by a series of reflexes which trigger each other off in a cyclical way, since bursts of oesophageal contraction may be slowed down to occur at (still regular) intervals of only once every half-hour or so by increasing the content of magnesium ions in the medium.[168] It is difficult to imagine even a chain of reflexes that would work as slowly as this. The two cyclical activities of feeding on one hand and of irrigation and defaecation on the other may thus be related to rhythms maintained in the nerve cord by pacemakers in the oesophagus and the nerve cord itself. If there are two pacemakers maintaining two muscular activities it may well be asked if one can dominate the other. The answer seems to be that the oesophageal pacemaker may dominate the entire behaviour when producing a protracted burst of proboscis activity. If a worm is laid on the surface, for example, the irrigation-defaecation cycle is abolished while the movements of the proboscis and anterior segments dig the animal into the sand. It is interesting that the first movements to appear and to become rhythmic in the earthworm larva are also in the stomodeum.

It is possible to elicit protracted activity of the proboscis in *Arenicola marina* by injecting the animal with adrenalin. If the excised oesophagus is subjected to adrenalin it undergoes sustained contraction, but the same substance has an inhibiting effect on the activity of the body wall. Acetylcholine has much the same effect as adrenalin in both cases. Here may be the clue to the dominance of the oesophageal pacemaker over the other activities. There is no direct evidence that adrenalin can be produced by annelids, but at least the same effect was got with extracts of leech nerve cord, and cells which resemble those that are thought to do so in other animals have been demonstrated.

The function of the brain

With all these activities the brain seems to have little to do. The brain in *Arenicola* is small; the worm lives in a rather constant environment, and its activities are co-ordinated by automatic mechanisms in the nerve cord. One may well ask what function the brain has in annelid worms and whether in fact it ever acts as a 'brain' in the sense of dominating or co-ordinating the nervous activities of the body.

If the brain of *Arenicola marina* is removed so as not to damage the connexions of the nerve cord with the oeso-phagus or suboesophageal ganglion, movements in the mid-body region are affected. A similarly careful extirpation in *Nereis* accelerates irrigation.[160] When Maxwell removed the brain from *Nereis*, the animal would not feed normally or burrow, although the proboscis could function when stimulated, so that presumably brain removal cuts off con-nexions with the special sense organs of the head which might normally be expected to elicit these responses. Friedländer[59] found that a brainless earthworm was gener-ally restive. It burrowed reluctantly, but nevertheless could do so, and it could also crawl. Yerkes[176] and Heck found that, in earthworms that had learnt to turn in one direction at a 'T' junction, removal of the brain had no effect on this ability. Prosser,[128] on the other hand, found that the reaction to light of *Eisenia foetida* was governed by the brain. At medium light intensities the worm will normally turn the head away from the light. By sectioning the brain and con-nexions in various ways, Prosser concluded that while the general body photoreceptors stimulated the muscles on the same side to contract, tending to turn the body towards the light, impulses were amplified in some way in the brain so that larger impulses passed down the other side, making the head turn away. This does not occur at low light intensities, so that the animal then turns towards the light. All these results indicate that there is no real interference with motor ability on removing the brain, but that brain removal results in a sensory deficiency.

While many workers have studied the structure of the polychaete brain we owe a great deal of our knowledge to the comparative studies of Pruvot, Holmgren and Han-ström.[75] More recently, detailed studies of the brain in *Nephthys* have been made by Clark[24] and in *Nereis* by Defretin and other zoologists in France. Gilpin-Brown[65] has also described the nerves entering the brain in *Nereis*. Defretin has found that the distribution of the ganglionic nuclei of the brain of *Nereis* is closely similar in different species, and Clark finds it possible to homologize the ganglionic nuclei in the brains of *Nereis* and *Nephthys*. In all these brains the cell bodies lie towards the dorsal side, the central and lower parts being composed of a dense mass of fibres. The shape of the whole brain varies in accordance with the degree of development of the sense organs: the palps, antennae, eyes, nuchal organs, and the more diffuse single-cell receptors of the prostomium. Motile worms have relatively large brains, lobed in relation to the develop-ment of the ganglionic nuclei receiving impulses from the various sense organs. In worms of more sedentary habit the brain is commonly smaller.

Within the brain of many polychaetes there is a pair of mushroom-shaped bodies known as the corpora peduncu-lata, similar to those found in some arthropods. Each con-sists of a dense mass of cell bodies forming a cap over a stalk formed by a bundle of ascending or descending fibres usually associated with the palps. In fanworms they are vestigial. One can suggest that they correlate impulses re-ceived from the palps which must be important organs to many worms, but we have no detailed knowledge of their function.

The longitudinal nerve cords, giant fibres, fine-fibre tracts, the fibres crossing the segmental ganglia, as well as the decussating fibres in the oesophageal commissures and brain, all serve to co-ordinate the series of segmental units into a functioning body.

THE SENSE ORGANS AND BEHAVIOUR

CHARLES DARWIN played a piano, a bassoon, whistled and shouted at his earthworms, but apparently without effect.

The most complex sense organs are found in those poly-chaetes which lead an actively motile life, or in which orientation is especially important. Most of them are borne on the prostomium and are directly related to the brain as described in the preceding chapter. Sense organs are commonly found in pairs, one on each side of the body, so that impulses entering the nervous system from them may be compared and the source of stimulation located. *Nereis* in a dish moves its head from side to side, and a worm moving up the stem of a Y-shaped tube makes similar searching movements on reaching the junction. Worms which live buried in sand or mud, on the other hand, experience a less variable sensory world, and their sensory system tends to be simpler, and their behaviour more stereotyped. It is not only for mechanical reasons that burrowing worms so often have a prostomium devoid of cirri, or have poorly developed eyes.

Langdon[100] has described in some detail the sense organs of *Nereis virens*. Apart from the two pairs of eyes on the prostomium, she described simple tactile or chemosensory cells scattered singly or in groups over the epidermis. These cells have a distal process or processes penetrating the cuticle, and a basal nerve fibre entering the subepidermal plexus.

They are especially numerous on exposed surfaces: over the distal part of the palps, on cirri and tentacles, and round the mouth, and are sparse between the segments in folds of cuticle. There are also groups of a hundred or so cells with a distal refractory body grouped spirally round deep pits in the cuticle. Several hundred of these organs are scattered over the surface of the anterior segments and on the bases of the cirri, and they are presumably simple light receptors. There is an additional pair of specialized sense organs in *Nereis* situated on the prostomium behind the eyes. These are the nuchal organs, studied in some detail by Rullier[135] who suggested that they were chemoreceptors; in *Nereis* they are two ciliated transverse slots.

Nuchal organs form distinct pits or slots in some other polychaetes, and in archiannelids, opheliids, ariciids and capitellids they are eversible and have retractor muscles. In amphinomids they form frilly external outgrowths supported by a median backward extension of the prostomium known as the caruncle. A less prominent, but essentially similar, development of a caruncle is found in some spionids. Their nuchal organs may communicate with long ciliated bands down the back, known as the dorsal organs, very variable in form but quite distinctive in different genera. These are not to be confused with the short transverse bands of cilia which are concerned with the maintenance of the respiratory current.

Light receptors

Most polychaetes possess eyes or light receptors of some kind. Eyes are most commonly prostomial, but not always; small sabellids like *Fabricia*, and the metamorphosing larvae of sabellariids, walk backwards trailing their crowns behind them, and they have eyespots on the pygidium.

The light sensitive cells of polychaetes are commonly elongate with a distal refractory body or bodies and a basal nerve fibre. The 'spiral organs' of *Nereis* described above contain a hundred such cells, but in many polychaetes the cells may be found in smaller groups or even, as in some sabellid crowns, as single ommatidium-like structures.

E*

These are remarkably arthropod-like and may have a long rod-shaped crystalline refractory body surrounded by pigment cells. In some sabellids such ommatidia may be grouped into a kind of compound eye especially well developed in *Branchiomma*. Such eyes have a common corneal area, but no lens. In some other polychaetes, on the other hand, there are distinct lenses secreted by a number of cells in a chamber between the cuticle, which forms a cornea, and a cup-like arrangement of light sensitive cells forming a retina. The prostomial eyes of *Nereis* are like this, but they are best developed in the pelagic alciopids which have enormous, bulging eyes, with large spherical lenses. The structure of these bright red eyes was studied in some detail in the nineties of the last century. The elaboration of the lensed eye may be traced through the syllids, nereids and phyllodocids to their derivatives the alciopids. In *Ranzania*, for example, the eyes are simple pits; in *Syllis* the cup of light sensitive cells is filled with filaments secreted by each to form a refractory ball; in *Nereis* these secretions are conglomerated into a single crystalline lens which, however, still fills the cup; in alciopids, the lens lies freely. All these lenses are secreted and should not be confused with the refractory body or rod inside the light receptor cell. These structures have been described in some detail by Hesse.[86]

Compared with these eyes the light receptors of oligochaetes and leeches are poorly developed. The structure of the light sensitive cells is similar in that each contains a refractory body and a basal nerve fibre, but they are mostly rounded cells lying towards the base of the epidermis. Hess[85] suggested that the irregularly shaped refractory body directed the light on to a dense reticulum of neurofibrillae which joined to form the basal nerve fibre. While similar to the light sensitive cells of polychaetes in containing a refractory body, the shape of the cells, their position in the epidermis and the development of neurofibrillae are different. These cells are also found singly, scattered over the epidermis, especially on the dorsal side and towards the anterior end, but groups forming more distinct eyespots are found in freshwater naidids and in leeches. In leeches there are commonly four or five eyes on each side of the most anterior segments, the arrangement being quite characteristic of certain families.

Light sensitive cells have been studied in oligochaetes by Hess[85] who found, in addition, groups of similar cells forming nodules in the nerve cord and in the distal parts of the nerves collecting fibres from the subepidermal plexus of the prostomium. These cells in the nervous system itself are apparently activated by decrease in light intensity, and Unteutsch[154] has contrasted their function in appreciation of shadow with those cells in the epidermis which are actuated by light increase. It is interesting that the cells in the nerve have a maximum sensitivity to yellow light, those in the epidermis to blue. Earthworms that have been studied show a negative phototaxis when subjected to light of high intensity, but positive to low. Removal of the prostomium results in a positive phototaxis at all intensities, however, and removal of the brain or severance of the nerve cord considerably increases the intensity at which phototaxis becomes positive.[85] Hess also discovered that if a worm was cut in two parts, the anterior part reacted negatively to ordinary daylight, the posterior part positively. Much the same reaction may be found in leeches which may change their reaction when hungry. It is not established that leeches can distinguish colours, though Kowalewski's statement that *Placobdella costata* is green or brown according to background suggests that they may. Smith[143], however, found in *P. parasitica* that the chromatophores responded to simple changes in light intensity.

The reversal of light reaction at low intensities in earthworms tends to bring them to the surface at night and keep them concealed within their burrows during the day. Most feed more at night, though some, such as *Eutyphoeus waltoni* studied by Bahl,[5] seem to have a greater tolerance of light and are more diurnal in habit. Searching the epidermis with a narrow pencil of light has shown that most earthworms are more sensitive to light over the dorsal and anterior surfaces than elsewhere.

The presence of cells which are stimulated by a decrease rather than an increase in light intensity in oligochaetes, is paralleled by the responses to shadows given by certain polychaetes. As in oligochaetes these reactions are clearly separate from those produced by light increases. The 'shadow reflex' is shown by many sabellids,[86] and has been studied in *Branchiomma* by Nicol.[118] A quick reaction to a shadow such as might be cast by a fish has obvious survival value if the crown of the worm is displayed in daylight. *Branchiomma*, which has very large compound eyes, is more diurnal in habit than many other sabellids in which the shadow reflex is not as marked or absent. *Branchiomma* orients its tube towards the light and shows a rapid response to decrease in light intensity by retraction into its tube. In the laboratory, *Branchiomma* rapidly acclimatizes to switching off the light, but the same worms will still give a response to a shadow caused by passing a card in front of the light for a few seconds. This occurs also in *Nereis pelagica*: habituation to one stimulus, in this instance turning off the light, was quite separate from shading. The serpulid *Hydroides*, collected intertidally, is said to react readily to shadows when in a dish, but those collected from 10 fathoms do not react as readily.

It must also be mentioned that whilst *Branchiomma* orients its tube with respect to the light, not all sabellids do so; *Sabella spallanzanii*, for example, orients its tube so that the crown can be freely twirled.

Light production

Several groups of polychaetes and some oligochaetes produce luminescent substances. Some earthworms exude a luminous slime from the anus or mouth when irritated, or in response to vibration, and such reactions may have some protective value. Some species of *Eisenia* and *Enchytraeus* do this when handled. In some instances the luminous material may be due to micro-organisms in the coelomic fluid which escapes through the dorsal pores. It has been suggested that this is the cause of the glow produced by *Chilota*, but in *Microscolex* Skowron[141] found that the luminous material was contained in coelomocytes which escaped from the anus through the enteronephridial system. Luminous slime is also produced by chaetopterids, by some nereids, syllids, cirratulids and terebellids, whilst in the scales of many scaleworms there are distinct photogenic organs under direct nervous control.

In *Chaetopterus* it is difficult to see what function the production of light has, since the animal lives permanently in an opaque tube. If removed from the tube the whole body glows brilliantly, and this is caused by luminous material actively secreted into the water by specialized glands situated in particular regions. Sie, Chang and Johnson[139] found that the production of luminous secretion from the aliform notopodia was influenced by pressure but not by temperature. Bonhomme[14] and Nicol[120] found that the cells secreting the luminous material were invested by a thin protoplasmic layer which dyed like muscle but lacked the birefringence characteristic of fibrous protein. Nicol[120] found that it was possible, by repeated stimulation, to fatigue the exuding mechanism whilst the glands themselves were still well charged with material. After such exhaustion of the photic response, it took about five hours before flashes could again be evoked, and three to four days for recovery following complete exhaustion. There is no doubt that the glands in the aliform notopodia are under nervous control: nerve fibres supplying the glands have been identified and waves of luminescent flashes can be induced by stimulation of the nerve cord and interrupted by its transection.

In *Chaetopterus* there is an appreciable time-lag between stimulation and production of a flash of light, and this is partly due to the light being generated only after the material has been extruded from the cell. Bonhomme suggested that this may be so also in the terebellid *Polycirrus*,[89] but Johnson and Johnson[89] have shown that the glow produced by this worm consists of a series of flashes, each of about one-tenth of a second duration. In *Chaetopterus* Johnson[89] found that the mechanism of light emission from the discharged slime was specific and not the same as in other instances of light production, and that the components were certainly exuded in particulate form, the light decaying soon after secretion.

The scales or elytra of many scaleworms also respond to a single stimulation of the elytral nerve by a series of rhythmical flashes which increase in intensity by some form of facilitation. The photogenic organs are on the undersides of the elytra, and are supplied from a ganglion on the elytral nerve coming from the nerve cord.[14, 121] At high frequencies of stimulation (more than 25/sec) the individual flashes merge into a continuous glow. While a single impulse in the nerve cord initiates the response, there is evidence to suggest that the flashes are kept going by a circuit of peripheral excitation from a ganglion in the elytra. When this is absent only one flash is produced in response to each stimulus. These responses may be elicited from detached scales, but in the intact worm stimulation of one part of the body may result in flashing in another. There is also some polarization of the nerve cord in this respect, for if a scaleworm is cut in half it is the posterior part which flashes while the anterior part crawls away. This could be regarded as a 'sacrifice lure'.[121]

In *Odontosyllis* light production has an undoubted sexual function. *Odontosyllis enopla* in Bermuda and *O. phosphorea* off British Columbia both show sharp lunar periodicity in their spawning—a subject discussed in the next chapter. The females produce a brilliant luminescence which attracts the males which also produce light; luminous products and eggs are shed into the water and the light then fades. The photogenic organs consist of groups of cells in the base of each parapodium discharging their contents by a duct opening ventrally near the tip. In some other syllids it would seem that there are photogenic cells scattered in the epidermis.

Some truly pelagic polychaetes also produce light and have distinct photogenic organs in the parapodia. In tomopterids they are modified coelomostomes; their glows are also said to be intracellular. Some alciopids, too, are known to luminesce and also have organs of a presumed photogenic function in the parapodia. Many of these pelagic forms are sparsely distributed in the ocean, many are abyssal or at least live below the photic zone, and it may well be that the development of photogenic organs in the alciopids is correlated with their relatively enormous eyes.

Other sense organs

Lack of experimental evidence makes the conclusion concerning the function of single-cell epidermal receptors somewhat uncertain, but those presumably tactile in function are abundant on cirri and tentacles. Anterior tentacles arising from the prostomium, and tentacular cirri derived from the anterior parapodia, are particularly well developed in the more active polychaetes, and are mostly paired so that a comparison can be made between the two sides. In such worms the pygidium also commonly bears a pair of anal cirri, which are developed too in some burrowers such as the maldanids and opheliids which lie with the anus near the surface. Dorsal parapodial cirri are variably developed and are often prominent, alternating with elytra in many scaleworms. Worms tend to have such structures reduced or absent when adapted for burrowing; their environment is more homogeneous and less interesting.

The sense cells on these tentacles or cirri are commonly fusiform in shape with a sensilla or sensillae projecting through the cuticle, and a basal nerve fibre. Such cells are scattered over the whole surface, and are numerous on specialized papillae such as occur on the elytra of many scaleworms; their nerves may be traced back into the segmental nerves, and from the palps of such worms as *Nereis*, directly to the brain. There is a subepidermal plexus

of fibres related to single sense cells in the epidermis of both
oligochaetes and leeches. These cells are sometimes aggre-
gated into distinct organs, especially prominent in naidids.
In *Stylaria* the prostomium is elongated into a highly
sensitive snout to which the animal owes its name, just as
the glossoscolecids owe their name to their long, slender
and tactile proboscis. Unlike the elongate prostomium of
Stylaria, the glossoscolecid proboscis may be drawn in and
out rather like a snake's tongue, as the animal moves about.
Single-cell receptors may be quite numerous in oliga-
chaetes, especially in the anterior dorsal region of the body.
Hesse[86] estimated that there were 700 of these /sq mm on
the dorsal side of the prostomium of *Lumbricus terrestris.*
Laverack[100a] has shown that the whole skin of earthworms
is sensitive to salt solutions and to touch, but only the
prostomial region to sweet substances such as sugar or
glycerol. Acid-sensitive receptors are also scattered over
the body surface,[100b] and these may be important in relation
to confining many species to soils of particular pH.

Leeches, as one might expect, react to stimulation by
their hosts, often in a very specific way. *Hemiclepsis mar-
ginata* is strongly attracted by mucus from its host, and
several other leeches (including *Hirudo* and *Glossiphonia*)
are attracted by and readily attach themselves to a test tube
containing water at 33°–35°C thrust into their tank. Kaiser[94]
found that *Hirudo* was very sensitive to temperature
differences, and Stammers[146] that the terrestrial leech,
Haemadipsa, would react to a man's hand when several
inches away. Many freshwater leeches are sensitive to
mechanical disturbance and when hungry will move towards
its source.

In leeches there are epidermal sense organs, first described by von Beyer after whom they are named, that are
quite unlike any found in other annelids.[67] These organs,
which are capable of great distortion, consist of a conical
cell just beneath the cuticle, related beneath to a sensory
nerve cell, and resting on and partly enclosed by another
cell with cross-striations. The suggestion has been made that

these are perhaps proprioceptors, and are sensitive to the great contortions of which the leech body is capable.

Statocysts of various kinds are also found in certain polychaetes: in several species of *Arenicola*, in several ariciids, in *Loimia* and *Lanice* amongst terebellids, and in several sabellids. All these are burrowers or tube-dwellers in which orientation may be very important. Apart from the ariciids which may have several pairs of statocysts, a single pair is most commonly found, usually situated in one of the most anterior segments. Three kinds of statocyst may be distinguished: two contain ciliated cavities, one of which is open and contains sand grains or other particles acting as statoliths; the other closed and enclosing a statolith which is secreted. The third kind, in which the statolith is also secreted, is a closed but non-ciliated capsule. All three types may be found in different species of *Arenicola*: *A. marina* has statocysts of the first, *A. cristata* the second, *A. grubii* of the third kind. Some other species are without them. Sabellids are provided with the closed, ciliated type. There is no doubt that these are all gravity receptors. *Branchiomma* and *Arenicola grubii* both normally lie vertically buried in the sand and right themselves if turned horizontally; removal of the statocysts abolishes this response.

The dull life of sand-eaters

Attention has already been drawn to the rather homogeneous environment of burrowing worms. The lugworm, *Arenicola marina*, lives in just such a uniform environment and its biology has been extensively studied by Wells. He found that a worm would live an apparently normal life in a narrow sand-filled tank in which it could be observed (fig. 16). This was immersed in a larger tank through which a flow of sea water was maintained at a constant level. By forming a partition in the worm tank between the burrow opening and the head shaft, the activities of the worm could be recorded on a kymograph by a lever actuated by a float in the chamber formed immediately above the burrow opening (see fig. 16). This chamber communicated to the outside tank by a capillary. Any activity of the worm affecting the float was recorded on the smoked drum. These recordings could be interpreted by watching the worm as the trace was being made. The trace produced formed a

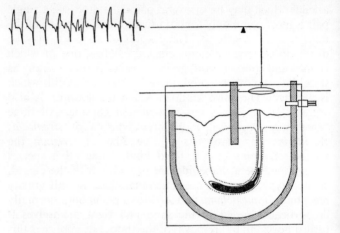

FIG. 16. *Arenicola marina* within a burrow made within a glass sandwich supported in a larger tank in which the water level is constant. Activities of the worm are recorded by means of the float actuating a lever writing on a smoked drum. Further explanation in the text. The trace was made over a period of 7 hr; at each downward spike the worm defaecated (trace redrawn from Wells)

regular pattern which resulted not only from the fact that activities such as feeding, defaecation and irrigation could not all be done at once, but that each was done in a regular cyclical way, as long as the worm was undisturbed. Wells has also found much evidence to suggest that this cyclical behaviour is not the result of a series of reflexes each initiating the next, but is due to spontaneous internal clocks in the central nerve cord and oesophageal plexus, to which reference has already been made. Excursion by the worm to the surface, for example, occurs normally as a preliminary to defaecation, and continues at similar intervals when the animal is fasting and the rectum empty.[161] Irrigation also continues when the body is surrounded by well-oxygenated water. *Arenicola ecaudata*, on the other hand, has rather different habits, and there is no evidence of an internal oesophageal pacemaker.

These cyclical activities can, of course, be interrupted: worms only show such regular behaviour when completely undisturbed. But *Arenicola marina* probably does remain relatively undisturbed for long periods, and this applies to some other annelids which burrow or live in tubes. Wells[167] has obtained equally regular recordings from *Chaetopterus* and from sabellids such as *Sabella spallanzanii*,[163] and it is quite likely that internal clocks govern their lives as well. We should not, perhaps, expect a worm leading a more active life and aware of a more varied sensory world to show such regularity in its behaviour, but even *Nereis*, when enclosed in a glass tube under as uniform conditions as are possible in a self-recording irrigation apparatus, shows spontaneous initiation and cessation of its activities.

Tube building

This does not mean that these animals act like machines. Many sand-dwellers have varied and often complex behaviour patterns and are capable of limited learning. Some that build tubes have a marked ability to select materials suitable for their purpose, the character of the tube depending on the species as much as on the materials available. The tube-building habits of many polychaetes have been described by Arnold Watson.[158] The terebellid 'sand mason' *Lanice conchilega* will incorporate a wide variety of materials in its tube, but many sabellids use only sand grains within a relatively narrow size-range for this purpose. The palm for this ability must surely go to the various species of *Pectinaria* which build tubes of shell fragments or sand grains carefully oriented and fitted together to give a smooth surface to the slender conical tube. *Owenia*, too, selects only flat pieces of shell or sand, and these are arranged on an organic secreted base like the tiles on a roof. Even when living in sand with few fragments suited to its purpose, these are still selected. Amongst the oligochaetes some naidids have rather similar habits; *Aulophorus* builds tubes from the spores of *Azolla* and *Salvinia*.

General behaviour

Polychaete worms such as *Nereis*, to which varied stimuli are likely to have some meaning, show more complex responses.[25] *Nereis pelagica* habituates after the first response to many stimuli, such as light increase or decrease, and to shadows; and the approach of a predator, for example, may be recognized by a complex of stimuli rather than by any token stimulus as in *Branchiomma*. The aggressive behaviour of *Nereis* is also interesting in its variety. *Nereis caudata* may fight members of its own sex, but not that of the opposite sex, whilst Clark[25] found that individuals of *N. pelagica* were aggressive towards other worms over the occupancy of tubes in the laboratory, but not when encountered in an open dish. In this instance fighting had no relation to the sex of the individual.

Many worms show thigmotactic responses, and in addition to being generally negatively phototactic are sometimes attracted towards dark areas. *Nereis diversicolor* follows a spiral course in a circular dish towards a black, vertically placed cylinder in the middle, and scaleworms such as *Halosydna gelatinosa* and *Gattyana cirrosa* will move towards black cards placed on the sides of a white dish evenly illuminated from above. Thigmotaxis is often observed in a dish: such worms as nereids and scaleworms tend to seek and to remain along the sides or edges where their bodies make maximum contact with other surfaces. Earthworms are also thigmotactic, positively geotactic, and move towards and remain in areas of high humidity.

Commensals

A positive response to dark areas combined with thigmo-taxis may help some scaleworms to find and remain under stones and in dark crevices. This habit may have led to many becoming commensal in the burrows and tubes of other animals, including those of other worms. Some are even found in the mantle cavities of molluscs: *Arctonoë vittata*, for example, occurs in the keyhole limpet, *Diodora aspera*, on the American west coast. No doubt these associations arose fortuitously, but recognition factors may then have been established, especially where the association became specific. Some commensals are found with a variety of different hosts and also living freely, and this suggests that for them the attracting stimulus is a general one. Some polychaetes are found commensal with echinoderms, with large burrowers such as the echiuroid *Urechis*, and with some crustaceans which maintain permanent burrows. The list of commensals is a long one, and some instances such as the harbouring of *Nereis fucata* by the hermit crab *Eupagurus bernhardus* will no doubt be familiar.

Such commensal relationships have been much studied in recent years by Davenport and his collaborators. He found, for instance, that the scaleworm *Arctonoë fragilis* was attracted by water from a tank occupied by the host starfish *Evasterias troschelii*, but not from those occupied by other starfishes, and further that if the host is later removed from the tank the water loses its attraction after a few hours. The *Arctonoë* also does not respond if the host is enclosed in a dialysing bag. Using a variety of types of apparatus, the ability of commensal worms to discriminate water flowing from the normal host has been studied, and also the effect of such stimulation on behaviour.[45] It is not known what the attracting factors are but it is clear that once the commensal habit has been acquired the response may be a very specific one.

Learning

So far we have considered only innate behaviour and the varied stimuli to which worms may respond. While experiments demonstrating speed of habituation to repeated stimulation have also been mentioned, it remains to be considered how far worms can modify their behaviour by other forms of learning.

Darwin probably attributed a greater learning capacity to earthworms than they possess, though they are capable of limited learning and can remember, for a short time, a learnt response. Darwin believed that worms draw leaves down into their burrows by the point. Hanel's experiments with triangles of various dimensions, in which she postulated an ability to distinguish the lengths of the respective sides, were later questioned by Jordan and could well be repeated again. Jordan concluded that the way in which an earthworm tries to drag a leaf down into the burrow is quite random; if the first attempt fails, another position will be tried, the pointed end being most likely to be successful. Málek[107] repeated these experiments and found that if the leaf were firmly held, so that the worm was unable to pull it down, it gave up after twelve to fifteen tries in different positions. While another leaf would be tackled immediately with equal persistence, the worm could never be persuaded to tackle the first leaf again.

This is suggestive of some limited learning, although refusing the leaf on which its own mucus has been liberally left could be innate. Yerkes[176] working with *Eisenia foetida*, and later Heck,[99] working with *Lumbricus terrestris*, found that worms could be taught to choose one limb of a Y-junction when an unpleasant stimulus was encountered in the other limb. Both found that memory was not dependent on the presence of the brain, for this could be removed without interfering with the learnt reaction. Conditioned reflexes can still be elicited after amputation of the anterior dozen segments in the earthworm. Krivanek's[99] experiments with *Lumbricus* are also interesting in this regard. He trained worms to turn in one direction while crawling freely on a glass plate, by presenting them with a stimulus such as a bright light from which they turn away, or a dim light towards which they will turn. When placed within a T-maze, such trained worms would tend to turn in the learnt direction on reaching the junction. After two to four training periods, for example, each involving 42 runs with sudden presentation of a light of 9·7 mc intensity from the same side, 73·6% would turn in the same direction in the maze without stimulation. This tendency would persist for two to three days after the training period, without reminders.

Conditioned reflexes can be induced also in polychaetes such as *Nereis*. *Nereis virens* will leave its burrow in response to a light alone after only six presentations of food accompanied by a light stimulus at 15–20 sec intervals, and it is possible to reverse the normal response by such conditioning to food. *Nereis* is as capable as the earthworm of learning a Y-shaped or T-shaped maze. But even individuals of the same species differ in their learning capacity at different times of day. Earthworms have definite activity cycles,[131] and it is interesting that worms learn a T-maze quicker at night, when they are normally more active, than during the day. We are only beginning to understand these phenomena.

8

REPRODUCTION AND DEVELOPMENT

WHILST the segmental plan of the annelid body can lead to serial repetition or serial variation, the facts described in the preceding chapters emphasize the fact that the segments are integrated into a single functional unit. If the anterior end of *Chaetopterus* is cut off anywhere as far back as the fourteenth segment, so that the most specialized and varied segments are removed, each of these segments will be exactly regenerated; and if a single segment is isolated from within this region, this will regenerate both anteriorly and posteriorly to form an exact copy of the original.[10] If, instead of fourteen, the first fifteen segments are removed, no regeneration whatever takes place.

The capacity for regeneration in annelids is generally well developed: combined with fragmentation it has led to asexual reproduction; and fragmentation, when related to gamete production, has given rise to specialized sexual individuals, often quite different from the parent stock.

Reparative regeneration

Most annelids have a definite number of segments characteristic of the species, and this number is usually attained early in development when the worm is quite small. In many worms the number is approximate, but in some maldanids like *Clymenella* or syllids such as *Syllis gracilis* or *Procerastea*, the number is the same in all adults. The actively growing zone is in front of the pygidium, and segments are proliferated forward in the young larva until the adult number of segments is attained. Each segment later enlarges. If the posterior end of the body is lost, a circumstance likely to occur to many worms in nature, the worm loses this potentially growing tissue, and consequently the pygidium appears early in subsequent regeneration. The rate at which the new segments are formed is greatest at first and gradually decreases. The part which remains after amputation must be able to maintain itself during regeneration, and the amount of posterior regeneration may be limited if amputation occurs so far forward that nephridia or endoderm are absent.[124]

Regeneration of a head when this is lost presents a rather different problem. Heads are not readily regenerated by either nereids or phyllodocids, though these are often found with regenerating tails. Archiannelids also have a poorly developed ability for anterior regeneration. On the other hand, sabellids and syllids do well, and so does the tropical earthworm, *Perionyx*. Even some leeches can regenerate the head under favourable conditions, so this ability is not related to complexity of the missing part. The regeneration of an operculum, when this is amputated in serpulids, affords an interesting instance demonstrating the coherence of the annelid body. When the operculum of *Vermiliopsis* or *Apomatus* is removed, it is replaced by proliferation from the stem of an existing crown filament. Ludwig and Ludwig[102] have made a study of this in *Hydroides*.

The ability to regenerate the whole body from a single segment seems exceptional. It is curious that *Chaetopterus* can do it when it is remembered that the body has such a diverse structure. *Myxicola*, another highly specialized worm, can also regenerate from a single segment, although for both *Chaetopterus* and *Myxicola* it is probable that the need will rarely arise. In both *Ctenodrilus* and *Dodecaceria caulleryi*, on the other hand, the body fragments spontaneously, and each segment so separated regenerates head and tail to form a complete new individual. The amount regenerated is generally dependent on the amount of material left to be dedifferentiated and utilized. *Dodecaceria caulleryi* is remarkable for its ability to produce a series of individuals from an isolated segment, the anterior regenerate breaking off to form a new tail, the posterior to form a new head, the 'parent' segment repeating the process once or twice until all its reserves have been used. The dependence of regeneration on material available is emphasized by the effect of repeated amputation. *Lumbriculus* has been found capable of regenerating the head twenty-one times in succession, the tail twice as frequently, the number being apparently limited only by the amount left to regenerate. If both ends are cut from a *Clymenella*, so that about a dozen segments are left, the number of segments regenerated anteriorly and the number posteriorly correspond to the position of the piece in the original body: an anterior piece regenerating more segments at its posterior end, and vice versa.

In regeneration of a head or of a tail, the wounded surface first seals and then a blastema of tissue is formed over the wound. In some syllids such as *Typosyllis prolifera* the two sides of the body are proliferated as separate parts which later fuse together in the mid-line (fig. 17F). The blastema is contributed by the mesoderm covered by cells from the ectoderm. The ectoderm of the part regenerated is proliferated from the parent ectoderm, the mesoderm by the mesoderm, and the gut from endoderm migrating into the blastema. In many worms, neoblast cells of mesenchymal origin play an important part in the regeneration of the mesoderm. This is so in *Chaetopterus*, and in *Aricia*, and it seems general in aquatic oligochaetes.[80] Moreover these neoblast cells may give rise to tissues other than those originally derived from mesoderm. Stephan-Dubois,[147] for example, has maintained that in *Nereis diversicolor* not only is the mesoderm regenerated from these mesenchyme cells, but other tissues as well. She found that all the missing parts are built up from mesenchyme cells which migrate towards the damaged areas, both in *Nereis diversicolor* and in *Lumbriculus*. On the other hand, no evidence has been found for the repaired tissues being derived from cells other than those of their own parent layer, following decapitation in *Salmacina*. The same thing occurs in *Polydora*.[153] The role of neoblasts certainly deserves further study.

In most worms the size of the blastema and of the regenerate is dependent on the position of the cut, the size decreasing posteriorly. Okada[124] found this to be so in various species of *Autolytus*. Moment[10] found that in *Eisenia foetida* three segments are regenerated if the head and the front 3–5 segments are removed; four if segments 6–10 are removed, and ten if the cut is made halfway down the body. Farther back progressively fewer segments are regenerated and from the twentieth segment backwards, none at all. The decrease is not even and gradual, but occurs in steps. In *Autolytus pictus* a head and five segments are regenerated if the cut is made at the fifth and only three or four segments are regenerated; between segments 13 and 42 only the head, and from segment 43 backwards only a cap of tissue forms over the wound.[124] *Lumbricillus variegatus*, on the other hand, will regenerate five to nine segments however many anterior segments are removed, and *Syllis spongicola* only the head and two segments,[124] whatever the level of amputation. It is as though the essential part which is lost is contained in this regenerate, for the adult number of segments is then attained by renewed pygidial growth. The prostomium and the new segments are generally formed in sequence, but there are instances where the new segments appear more or less simultaneously from the blastema. This occurs in the maldanid, *Axiothella mucosa*, although in *A. rubrocincta* replacement is sequential. The rate of replacement may also be dependent on the distance of the cut from the head end. Berrill found no such dependence in *Sabella*, and there is clearly much variety in these phenomena.

In regeneration of the anterior end, the stomodeum is reconstituted from an ectodermal invagination to meet a forward growth from the old gut. There are apparent exceptions to this. But in every case, with the formation of a new head some sort of control of anterior segment form and number seems to be re-established, for where the total number of segments is not replaced from the blastema, the most anterior of the old segments metamorphose into those of their new positions, and the total segment number is made up by renewed activity just in front of the pygidium. This may involve complete changes in the morphology of the old anterior segments, as it does, for instance, in oligochaetes such as *Lumbricillus variegatus* (where not more than nine new segments are formed anteriorly, wherever the cut is made), or in *Sabella*, where the neuropodial and notopodial chaetae are reversed in the anterior segments. Because of this particular differentiation in sabellids, it is possible to follow the course of metamorphosis rather easily, and this has been done by Berrill, Gross and Huxley, and Berrill and Mees.[10] In *Sabella* only the prostomium, peristomium and a single additional segment are regenerated anteriorly, even if the cut is made towards the posterior end of the body. Berrill suggested that this anterior region once reconstituted has a reorganizing effect on the remainder of the body, which, metamorphosing into the new correct segment order, obviates the need for further delimitation of segments from the blastema. This has been studied in more recent years by Vannini and Ranzoli.[157] They have found that with posterior pieces there is often an 'overshoot', the new thoracic region having more segments than it should. A further sidelight on this phenomenon is shown by the result of repeated amputation of the head which has a summation effect on the number of posterior segments metamorphosing into anterior ones. Berrill interprets this as indicating that the factor influencing metamorphosis acts from the posterior surface of the metamorphosed segment. But this phenomenon is rather puzzling, for under some circumstances 'segment stepping' occurs, for some more posterior segments metamorphose beyond one or more that do not. There is also a remarkable independence of the two sides of the body, for, if a cut is made only on one side, metamorphosis of the segments occurs only on that side.

Berrill's suggestion that the reconstituted 'head' region following anterior amputation in *Sabella* has a reorganizing effect on the remainder of the body is interesting when seen in the light of the more recent studies of Herlant-Meewis[81] on *Aelosoma viridis*. Herlant-Meewis distinguishes a 'cephalic region' which is alone replaced when amputation of the anterior end is made, and a 'cephalic territory' which is a more extensive part within which there is an ability to regenerate the 'cephalic region'. The same sort of thing occurs in *Lumbricillus* and *Syllis spongicola*.

Another interesting aspect of such regeneration is the importance of the nervous system, and indeed how this is itself regenerated presents many unsolved problems. Okada[125] has found that a new head may be induced to form at any level in the body by transection of the nerve cord. Regeneration in *Eisenia foetida* and *Allolobophora caliginosa* is dependent on the presence of nervous tissue, as has been confirmed by transplanting pieces of nervous system. Herlant-Meewis[84a] has demonstrated replacement cells in the nerve cord of *Eisenia foetida*. The new brain forms itself anew in a dorsal position and then re-establishes connexion with the nerve cord. If the nerve cord is severed just behind the suboesophageal ganglion, and the nerve cord hooked out of a hole made in the side of the body, a lateral head and a few anterior segments will be formed. While early reconstitution of a brain, to which an inductive role has been attributed, seems common in other groups of animals, this is not true of *Salmacina*. Against these uncertainties the work of Herlant-Meewis[82] is of especial interest. She has found good evidence that, in aelosomatids, the tissue of the nerve cord induces the formation of the brain, and that this then induces the regeneration of the structures of the head. During normal asexual reproduction in *Chaetogaster*, on the other hand, the brain and circumoesophageal commissures are formed first. The work of Holmes on *Nereis*, and Zhinkin on *Rhynchelmis*, also showed the importance of the nervous system in posterior regeneration.[10] The apparent inductive role of the nervous system in regeneration suggests that this may be a neurosecretory phenomenon.

Asexual reproduction

It is perhaps not surprising that the ability to regenerate lost parts is accompanied by a capacity to reproduce asexually. Regeneration of a complete individual from artificially separated segments is possible in *Dodecaceria* and in *Ctenodrilus*, and this ability is used naturally in production of new individuals, for fragmentation of the body into single segments or short sections occurs spontaneously. Orderly fragmentation occurs in some syllids and in spionids such as *Pygospio*, and even in some sabellids such as *Sabella spallanzanii*, but instances of spontaneous disintegration are much rarer than those in which only the posterior part of the body breaks off to form a new individual. The position of the break is usually precisely determined and may often be recognized by an epidermal ingrowth and formation of a 'macroseptum' forming a white line across a particular segment. In the syllids *Procerastea* and *Myrianida* this occurs initially at the fourteenth segment, and then, proceeding posteriorly, after the following two, then three, then four, followed by an indefinite number of new individuals at initially three-segment intervals. In *Chaetogaster diaphanus* it is in the anterior part of the fifth segment that the macroseptum appears, the posterior part of the old fifth segment contributing the head of the new individual. The anterior part of the old fifth segment continues to grow by becoming a new pygidium and proliferating new segments forward, further divisions by macrosepta occurring as before, when the appropriate segment number is attained. Malaquin[106] has a drawing of a *Myrianida* with a total of twenty-nine individuals, or stolons as these may be called, complete with heads, attached to the parent stock. The site of the new head is determined even within a segment. Okada[125] found that if the stolon was cut off at the anterior end of the fourteenth segment of the parent or stock, a new head regenerated from the wound in the normal way, so that the stolon then had two heads narrowly separated by half the original segment (fig. 17B).

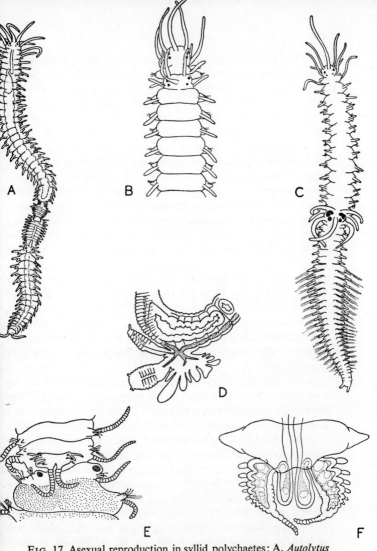

Fig. 17. Asexual reproduction in syllid polychaetes: A, *Autolytus prolifer* with a chain of stolons (redrawn from Thorson); B, *Autolytus pictus*, regeneration of two heads by transection of the 14th segment (redrawn from Okada[125]); C, formation of a dissimilar male stolon in *Autolytus* sp.; D, a median L.S. showing production of multiple stolons by *Trypanosyllis gemmipara* (redrawn from Potts[126]); E, regeneration of the pygidium in front of the head of the stolon in *Syllis vittata* (redrawn from Durchon[49]); F, posterior regeneration in *Typosyllis prolifera* showing independence of the two sides (redrawn from Okada[124])

There is a bewildering variety of different methods of proliferating new individuals, but space does not permit more than brief mention of some of them (fig. 17). Pioneer work in this field was done by Malaquin, Potts and Okada,[125] to whose publications the reader is referred, and to the discussion of this work by Berrill.[10] The genus *Trypanosyllis*[49, 126] shows great variation from one species to another (fig. 17D). *Trypanosyllis prolifera* can produce heads from almost any segment and chains of new heads occur on consecutive segments; *T. asterobia* forms clusters of stolons each of which grows out from a single segment; *T. crosslandi* has a proliferating prepygidial zone producing bunches of stolons, new ectoderm, mesoderm and endoderm being formed from specially active cells derived from each layer.[126] *Syllis ramosa* can also produce lateral buds, and in this instance the new individuals remain attached to the parent sufficiently long for them to be of comparable size and to have themselves produced further lateral individuals. The resulting tangle of bodies has been found in sponges, the lateral buds projecting into the side chambers of the sponge; McIntosh described it from the Challenger collections.

Some aquatic oligochaetes also reproduce asexually by essentially similar means. As in polychaetes, simple fragmentation is relatively rare, but effectively increases the population when it does occur. It has been calculated that a single *Nais paraguayensis* could give rise to 15,000 individuals within two months, but the efforts of most species are more modest. Apart from this species of *Nais, Bothrioneurium* amongst tubificids, *Lumbriculus* and *Aulophorus* are well known to reproduce by the body breaking into fragments. Most naidids and aelosomatids produce stolons much like those of syllids in that the new individuals are well differentiated before breaking off. As in syllids there are distinct segments where new growth occurs, and as in *Trypanosyllis crosslandi*, for example, the new individuals are formed from the activity of 'blastocytes' derived from each layer and congregated in definite positions. From existing evidence this seems usual, and the derivation of all tissues from blastocytes of single origin reported by Herlant-Meewis[82] in *Aelosoma*, seems exceptional. In naidids the parental stock continues to produce new individuals or zooids for some time, and as each attains the segment number at which new zooids are produced, each then starts production of secondary zooids to form a chain. This also occurs in some aelosomatids (*Aelosoma hemprichi*), but in others (*A. viride*) production is more complicated.[12] In *A. viride* two zooids are first proliferated, these growing by multiplication of segments in the usual way, but the following zooids do not then grow in length but divide to give further zooids. There is as great a variety in these phenomena as in the syllids.[81, 82, 83]

The new individuals produced by any of these methods may be similar to the adult, or be produced for sexual reproduction and be quite different in appearance. Such sexual individuals are often better adapted for swimming up to the surface for spawning; those of *Autolytus*, for example, have long swimming chaetae and larger tentacles and eyes than the parent stock.

The variety of these events has led to many confusing terms; Herlant-Meewis[83] proposes the following, all of which come under the general heading of 'schizogony'. The fragmentation of an individual into two or more parts may be referred to as 'scissiparity', either before ('architomy') or after ('paratomy') formation of heads on the parts which break away. When these processes are related to the production of sexual individuals either comes under the heading of 'stolonization', although stolons are often formed in another way. Instead of division of an existing body, new individuals may be formed by production of a new pygidial bud with a renewal of segment proliferation (what English writers have called 'gemmiparity', and French 'bourgeonnement pygidial'). Both scissiparity and pygidial budding may occur together in either stock or stolon, and it is to this fact that many varieties of schizogony are due (fig. 18).

Some facts of regeneration suggest that the process may

F

be under neurosecretory control. It is natural to ask whether
the whole process of asexual reproduction, maintenance of
the number of segments and metamorphosis of sexual
stolons is not also under the control of hormones. In
this connexion the work of Durchon[50] is of especial
interest.

Abeloos first showed that stolonization is evoked by the
removal of the anterior end of the body in *Syllis prolifera*,
and Durchon has demonstrated that the formation of
stolons in *Trypanosyllis zebra* and *Syllis amica* is stimulated
by removal of the proventriculus. He also found that the
number of segments in the stolon bears a constant relationship to that of the stock, and that the more posterior segments have a greater potentiality for development of
gametes than those more anterior. More recently, Durchon[49, 50] has reinvestigated asexual reproduction in
different species of *Trypanosyllis*. The multiple stolons of
T. asterobia, each of which springs from a single adjacent
segment, arises first as a head which then induces the
formation of a pygidial bud immediately in front of it.
In this genus a series may be traced from *T. coeliaca*, in
which simple paratomous stolonization occurs, to *T.
asterobia*, in which each segment forms a new head and
pygidial bud in front. In *T. gemmipara* the pygidial bud is
multiple so that many stolons are produced from one or
two adjacent segments as described by Potts.[126]

Epitoky and its control

Anyone who has caught the swimming sexual individuals of
syllids at a light held over the water will have been im-
pressed by their beauty and often great difference from the
secretive bottom 'asexual' individuals from which most of
them are budded. Sexually mature nereids are very similar,
but they are not produced as stolons; they are bottom-living
worms which have metamorphosed to enable them to swim
towards the surface for spawning. The parapodia and
chaetae become effective paddles and the eyes become

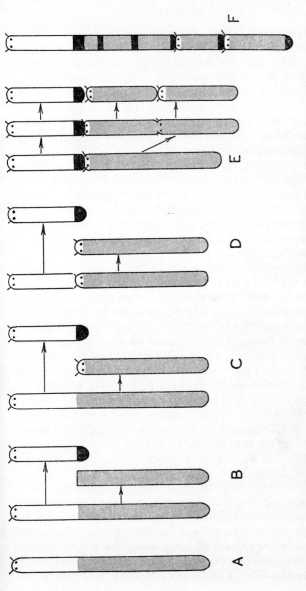

Fig. 18. Budding and stolon formation in polychaetes (modified after Herlant-Meewis[83]); gamete-bearing part stippled (often metamorphosed), pygidial regeneration black: A, an epitoke ('heteronereid' or 'heterosyllid'); B, gamete-bearing region breaking off (palolos); C, stolon regenerating a head after liberation; D, formation of new head and pygidium of stock before liberation of stolon; E, formation of a second stolon before liberation of the first; F, formation of multiple stolons

greatly enlarged. These metamorphosed nereids or epitokes were not at first associated with the bottom-living stages from which they are formed, and were first described as belonging to a new genus *Heteronereis*, just as the sexual stolons of *Autolytus* were first described as *Sacconereis* (female) and *Polybostrichus* (male). 'Heteronereids' are very reminiscent of the epitokes formed by some other syllids such as *Odontosyllis* and *Eusyllis monilicornis* which undergo metamorphosis in the posterior gamete-producing segments rather than budding off stolons.[106] Other syllids, such as *Syllis hyalina*, bud off sexual stolons, but these do not form a new head either before or after breaking away, a process similar to that found in the palolos. Additional or modified chaetae are formed in a number of other families.[26] Some amphinomids, phyllodicids, nephthyids and glycerids do so, to name but a few.

In the palolo worms, which belong to the family Eunicidae, the hind part rises to the surface writhing, headless and tail foremost. Even though headless the hind pieces are very sensitive to light intensity and are positively phototactic to intensities between 50 and 0·0005 ft. c. The time of their appearance on the surface of the sea can be predicted with some accuracy, a fact well known in different parts of the world to people who net them for food. The Pacific palolo (*Eunice viridis*) in the region of Fiji and Samoa, *Lysidice oele* in the Amboina region known as the 'Wawo', and the 'Atlantic palolo' (*Eunice schemacephala=fucata*) in the Dry Tortugas form spectacular swarms. The Japanese 'palolo' (*Tylorrhynchus heterochaetus*), also considered a delicacy, and known by a variety of names in different parts of Japan, is a nereid.

All possible variations in stolon production and metamorphosis are found in the syllids, and many early workers attempted to find some evolutionary sequence. But as Clark[26] pointed out, the way in which the new chaetae are formed in the epitoke of *Syllis spongicola*, for example, is quite different from that in nereids as described by Defretin and Bauchot-Boutin and Bobin. We seem to be dealing here with three phenomena: metamorphosis, asexual division and sexual development, all of which are independent or independently controlled, but by their nature are variously related in different worms. The process in the eunicids has certainly been evolved independently from that in nereids and syllids.

The changes which occur in formation of the hetero-nereis have been studied from different points of view. Usually the whole posterior part of the body undergoes metamorphosis, but in some nereids, such as *Nereis rava*, metamorphosis affects only the middle region of the body. In a few species where this occurs the posterior unmeta-morphosed part regresses or is thrown off before spawning; the Japanese 'palolo' *Tylorrhynchus* does this. The changes affecting the parapodia, chaetae, eyes and prostomium are obvious because they are external. Internal sarcolysis of some muscles, augmentation of others, and formation of new ones required for swimming, occur, together with an erosion of the gut to allow release of gametes through the anus. Defretin, Durchon, Bauchot-Boutin and Bobin have studied these processes in some detail, and their results are reviewed by Clark.[26]

Durchon[46, 47, 48] has shown that immature worms are prevented from metamorphosing into epitokous individuals by inhibitory hormones produced in the brain. The brain also inhibits gamete formation, whether accompanied by metamorphosis or not, a conclusion confirmed in *Platy-nereis dumerilii* by Hauenschild.[76, 77] Neurosecretory cells have been known to occur in the brain since Scharrer des-cribed them in *Nereis virens* in 1936, and it seems likely that the inhibitory hormone or hormones are produced by them. Evidence for this was found by Bobin and Durchon,[50] for the granules which accumulate at the base of the brain in *Perinereis cultrifera* disappear as the worms mature. A further circumstance suggests that this possible hormone is blocked by another produced by the gonads or gametes themselves. Durchon[46, 47] obtained a precocious metamor-phosis in 50% of immature *P. cultrifera* into which he injected oocytes, and Hauenschild[76] found, conversely, that the removal of the posterior gamete-producing end in *Platynereis dumerilii* retarded metamorphosis of the more anterior part.

There is also evidence that hormones produced by the brain influence posterior regeneration. Durchon,[50] and Clark and Evans[29] have found that posterior regeneration is poor in nereids which have been decapitated, unless the brain is reimplanted. They found evidence that hormones appear in the brain 48 hr after loss of the posterior segments, and that repair is in progress one day after this. If the brain is removed 48 hr after the posterior segments, however, sufficient hormone has been produced to stimulate repair. Clark has also shown that in *Nephthys* the cells in the blood greatly increase and take up neurosecretory material from the back of the brain during posterior regeneration following amputation.[50]

It will be recalled that stolonization is also under what is probably hormonal control, but in syllids it is the proventriculus, not the brain, which affects both sexual development and the formation of stolons. The existence of hormones is implied by the result of extirpation and implantation of the proventriculus in syllids, or brain in nereids, and by histochemical evidence. It remains to extract and purify the hormones involved and to cause the same effects by their injection. But a hypothesis of endocrine control of the processes of stolonization, metamorphosis and sexual development is a reasonable one, bearing in mind the variety of ways in which these three phenomena are associated. This variety, which at first seems so bewildering, could easily be accounted for by differences in hormonal control. Indeed, neurosecretion may be of major importance in the co-ordination of the annelid body, in segment growth and number, for neurosecretory cells have been demonstrated not only in adult *Harmothoë* but also in the young larvae.

Child thought the annelid body showed two physiological gradients, the more important decreasing posteriorly, the less important anteriorily. This may now be reconsidered in the light of the following facts: first, the presence of neurosecretory centres in the brain, and possibly elsewhere in the nerve cord, and secondly, the presence of a prepygidial zone of growth. Both may be interfered with by amputation, or by production of new pygidial buds. The observations of Cresp[31] are also interesting in this regard. The process of asexual reproduction in *Salmacina* sometimes leads to monsters of various kinds: worms with heads at both ends, heads facing each other in the middle of the body, or one with half a head on one side, may all be produced. These matters have been discussed at some length by Abeloos[2] who concludes that they may be explained by assuming that there are indeed two integrating systems: one ectoneural, the other mesodermal; the first predominating in anterior regeneration, the second in posterior. This reconciles the rather conflicting evidence of posterior reparative regeneration by mesenchymal neoblasts and anterior derivation of each layer as before, but we are not yet certain about the nature of these homeostatic mechanisms which maintain the annelid body as a whole, or those which disrupt its cohesion.

Swarming

The swarming of the sexual forms of both nereids and syllids generally occurs at night, and as in the palolos shows a lunar periodicity. Korringa[98] points out that all the worms which show such periodic spawning behaviour live in relatively shallow waters and are nocturnal in habit, and that when the spawning period is particularly sharp this is due to a coincidence of the diurnal, monthly and annual cycles which govern the behaviour of these worms. Spawning may occur on one night only of one or two consecutive months, but in many nereids the number found each night increases to a maximum over a period of a week or so. Hauenschild[77] has shown that metamorphosis in *Platynereis dumerilii* is

itself a photoperiodic phenomenon and that its synchronization with the lunar cycle disappears when worms are kept
under conditions of continuous illumination.

In most nereids, such as *Nereis succinea*, the males swim
to the surface first to await the females. When they appear
the males swim round them whilst emitting sperm. Sperm
emission is controllable and is usually elicited by the
presence of the female, the eggs being shed in response to
shed sperm. It has been suggested that this behaviour of the
male is dependent on sense organs in the dorsal parapodial
cirri, for when these are removed the males fail to orient
correctly to the female. The swirling vortices of males
around a female is a remarkable sight when seen by a light
suspended over the water. *Platynereis megalops*, which like
N. succinea may be seen spawning at Woods Hole in
Massachusetts, has a completely different fertilization
mechanism. It has probably evolved in relation to the
curious fact that the eggs are rendered unfertilizable after
only 30 sec contact with sea water. Here fertilization is internal; the male wrapping tightly round the female inserts
his anus into her mouth and injects the sperm. As the gut
of both has been eroded by phagocytes, the sperm pass
directly into the coelom of the female; the eggs are fertilized and shed almost at once from the posterior end of
her own body.

In syllids the swarms of *Odontosyllis enopla* in Bermuda
and *O. phosphorea* off Vancouver Island are famous, for
the females which reach the surface before the males are
strongly luminescent.[126]

Some nereids that have penetrated brackish or fresh
water do not swarm and have abandoned metamorphosis.
Nereis diversicolor is said to be 'atokous', the males and
females spawning in the burrows or on the surface of the
mud as described by Müller in 1771. Most larvae are not as
well equipped for osmoregulation as the adults. Some
species migrate downstream for swarming; *Nereis japonica*
does this; others such as *N. diversicolor* are limited in distribution by the salinities tolerated by the larvae,[144] and the

habitats presenting the most rigorous conditions are re-populated by older worms of each generation. The eggs in the freshwater *N. limnicola* are self-fertilized internally, and the larvae escape from the coelom when they are well grown and probably better able to withstand the osmotic conditions of the environment. It is interesting that all these species just mentioned are so closely related that Hartman regards them as synonymous. It is simplest to regard these nereids as having a potential for varied reproduction which can be exploited under different conditions. Self-fertilizing hermaphroditism in *N. limnicola* leads to genetic isolation, and we may expect the *N. japonica-limnicola-diversicolor* 'Rassenkreis' to diverge. *Platynereis massiliensis*, confused with *P. dumerilii* by Hempelmann, is another instance of divergence in reproductive method: *P. massiliensis* is atokous, *P. dumerilii* epitokous.[46]

Sex

Several hermaphrodite nereids are known to be found in fresh water, and most serpulids and occasional members of other families are also hermaphrodite. Durchon[49] has found that syllids show a general sex reversal from female to male, female stolons giving rise to male ones which occasionally give rise to female again rather than male. Hauenschild[50] has investigated this in *Grubea clavata* which does not form stolons, finding that fasting and rise in temperature influence the change from female to male. The eunicidan, *Ophryotrocha*, on the other hand, is protandrous, all worms being first male, then female. Dasgupta and Austin[43] have found evidence that the hermaphrodite serpulids *Spirorbis* and *Filograna* have been derived from triploids with a loss of a single chromosome, and it is tempting to suggest that self-fertilization may have arisen as a corollary of the difficulty of chromosome pairing. Other serpulids (*Hydroides, Pomatoceros*) are possibly tetraploids in which a pair of chromosomes has been lost. They are protandrous and hence cross-fertilizing.

G

Fertilization and development

Many methods to ensure a high percentage of fertilized oocytes have been evolved in polychaetes, apart from the synchronization of swarming already mentioned. Some phyllodocids lie together when spawning, the fertilized eggs being enclosed in a bag of jelly on the surface of the mud. Similar capsules are made by some ariciids such as *Scoloplos*. *Capitella* has special copulatory chaetae, and *Sternaspis* special copulatory appendages. Male *Pisone remota* have non-motile sperm which develop in a single specialized segment, the nephridia of the segment following being adapted as seminal vescicles and their ducts opening at the tip of elaborate copulatory organs. The nephridia of the genital segments in the female are adapted as receptacula in which the sperm are stored. Receptacula are also formed from modified parapodial cirri in female alciopids, doubtless a valuable adaptation considering the rarity of individuals in the plankton.

The protection of the fertilized eggs in jelly or in capsules of various kinds is adopted by many polychaetes. Several scaleworms are known in which the females retain the eggs and larvae under the scales, and spionids generally enclose their eggs in simple capsules, chains of which may be found in the burrow. Generally, many larvae emerge from a single capsule to feed. In serpulids the eggs of *Spirorbis borealis* develop in a string within the coiled tube of the parent; those of *S. pagenstecheri* in a special chamber formed by the operculum. In *Microserpula* paired calcareous ovicells containing the fertilized eggs are attached to the parent tube. Female syllids when swimming to the surface retain the oocytes in a thin pellicle from the opening of the ducts, either singly as in *Exogone* or *Sphaerosyllis* or in a single sac slung under the body as in *Autolytus*. *Parapionosyllis* retains the young larvae for some time in this way and so does the hermaphrodite *Pionosyllis*. Gravier[68] gives an interesting account of many such habits.

Larvae sooner or later escape, and many live for some

time in the plankton, a habit which helps to distribute the species. Most planktotrophic larvae develop from small eggs (100μ) which hatch quickly. Development from larger eggs (250μ) is carried further before hatching, and such larvae often never enter the plankton or swim freely for only a short time. Some spionid larvae, however, hatch late and remain in the plankton for as long as three months, and can within limits delay leaving it until they settle on a suitable substratum. They are often very selective about where they settle.[172]

The simplest trochophores are larvae with a single prototroch and a pygidial telotroch as described in chapter 1. After formation of a trochophore, segments are progressively delimited forwards from the pygidium. Small eggs usually give rise to such trochophores, but larger eggs may not hatch until three or more segments are already formed. There is great diversity of larval morphology in the Polychaeta, and the elegance and beauty of many of them cannot simply be conveyed in words. The trochophore itself may be elaborated, acquiring an apical sense organ and functional gut before any segments are recognizable, those of serpulids such as *Pomatoceros* or *Hydroides* being the most beautiful. In capitellids, on the other hand, a great many segments are delimited early in development. As segments are added the larva becomes more worm-like, sinks to the bottom, and the ciliated bands are lost. In other larvae the first chaetigerous segment may have hypertrophied chaetae which protect it from enemies, and perhaps also from sinking; spionid larvae, the larvae of sabellariids, and the 'mitrarias' of oweniids, are like this. In the 'mitraria' larva of *Owenia*, and in the archiannelid *Polygordius*, the trochophore is relatively large and elaborate and the structure of the adult worm is gradually differentiated within it, the trochophore being eventually demolished in *Owenia*, during a cataclysmic metamorphosis. Such instances of metamorphosis in *Owenia*[171] and in *Polygordius*[147] are specializations, and the development of most polychaetes is simpler and more direct.

Both the oliogochaetes and the leeches derived from them

are exclusively hermaphrodite, and have developed mechanisms whereby sperm from one is transferred to the other to be stored in spermathecae to fertilize the eggs when these are later laid. Concomitant with this development, the segments in which the male and female gametes are produced are distinctive. The arrangement of the gonads and spermathecae is a valuable taxonomic feature. In most polychaetes the gametes appear to arise in many segments from ill-defined tracts in the peritoneum, but those of oligochaetes arise in discrete gonads, and their ducts are permanent. The testes discharge their contents into the coelomic cavity of the segment in which they lie, acting as a seminal vesicle which may bulge into other segments when full. Complex behaviour patterns for copulation to ensure cross- and avoid self-fertilization have arisen. This was described in lumbricids by Grove, and Grove and Cowley.[72] The two worms lie head to tail, held together by their chaetae and by belts of mucus, within which the sperm are transferred to the openings of the partner's spermathecae. In megascolecids the copulants lie together in the same manner but direct transference of sperm is possible owing to the position of the respective pores, and to the development of a small papilla near the opening of the male duct which acts as an intromitant organ.

In *Pheretima posthuma*, the papilla is inserted into each of the three pairs of spermathecae of the copulant in turn, the whole process taking four to five hours. Enchytraeids and most aquatic oligochaetes pair in much the same way, but in tubificids the sperms are enclosed in elongate spermatophores secreted by the so-called 'prostate' glands. Prostates are also well developed in megascolecids. The vasa deferentia of many oligochaetes end in a terminal chamber and this may in some species be evaginated as a sort of penis. Distinct penes are present in some worms, those of *Alma* at maturity being relatively enormous and retractile within special chambers.

The leeches also exchange sperm, but in the gnathobdellids the exchange is often not simultaneous as these leeches tend to be protandrous. The reduction of the coelom has led to an even more clearly demarcated reproductive system than in the oligochaetes, a series of paired testes discharging their gametes into a single vas deferens on each side, the two vasa being enlarged or coiled into seminal vesicles before joining at a common median orifice. At this junction, accessory glands, an atrium, penis or ejaculatory structures may be found. Rhynchobdellids and pharyngobdellids have no penis, and the glands found near the male aperture are concerned with the elaboration of spermatophores. In *Erpobdella* the spermatophores are held in the male aperture when the sperm escape. In rhynchobdellids the fusiform spermatophores are 5–10 mm long and are implanted in a special area of the skin. The neck of the spermatophore contains a granular secretion which is thought to be a proteolytic enzyme which digests sufficient of the tissues for the sperm to gain entry into the partner's body. In piscicolids the spermatophore is an amorphous mass placed on the female aperture. The female aperture, like the male, is median, and is met by a duct on each side from a single pair of long ovisacs representing coelomic spaces into which the oocytes are shed. In leeches which implant spermatophores in the skin there is a cord of connective tissue joining the implantation area with the ovisacs down which the sperm pass, presumably in response to some chemical stimulus. These remarkable processes are described by Brumpt.[19] The relationship of this vector tissue, the implantation area and ovisacs seems very variable.

In all leeches egg laying occurs some time after copulation; in *Erpobdella* after a few days, in *Hirudo* anything up to nine months. In earthworms egg laying usually occurs after a day or two. In the African eudrilid earthworms the openings of the spermathecae and the oviducts are very close, in *Malodrilus*, indeed, the openings are together, so that fertilization is virtually internal. In both oligochaetes and leeches the eggs are laid in small batches within a cocoon secreted by a specialized part of the skin known as the clitellum. The clitellum may be recognizable throughout the year, or only at the breeding season. Herlant-Meewis[84] has studied its development in *Eisenia foetida*, and has found some evidence that these processes are under neurosecretory control. If pieces of clitellar epithelium of *Allolobophora* are transplanted into the skin of an immature worm, the transplant loses into clitellar development and merges with that of the host, and if a piece of epithelium of an immature worm is placed in the clitellar region of a mature worm it metamorphoses into clitellar tissue.

The cocoon is apparently proteinaceous, and filled with an albuminous material in which the eggs are laid, the two substances secreted by different cells in the clitellar epithelium.[72] The cocoon is secreted as an elastic belt, the worm sliding backwards out of it. As the worm does so, the eggs are laid and fertilized as they pass the spermathecal openings. The two ends of the cocoon close together as the head is withdrawn to form a lemon-shaped object. Aquatic oligochaetes have similar cocoons, but those of the glossoscolecid *Criodrilus* are long and fusiform and deposited in clumps on plant stems. In leeches the cocoons are often transparent or horny. *Glossiphonia* carries several attached to the ventral side of the body, the young remaining there for some time after hatching. Piscicolids attach their cocoons to stones; those of *Hirudo* are spongy masses 2–3 cm long deposited in damp places on the ground.

The eggs of freshwater oligochaetes are relatively large and yolky, so that the young worm hatches at an advanced state of development. The eggs of earthworms are more variable in size, the more primitive lumbriculids having fairly large yolky eggs, the most advanced lumbricids and megascolecids having far less yolk, the larvae feeding on albumin provided in the cocoon. In the leeches there is a similar difference between the large yolky eggs of the glossiphoniids and the relatively small eggs of the gnathobdellids. Even so, the development is far more direct in all oligochaetes and leeches than in any polychaete.

9

THE ORIGIN AND CLASSIFICATION OF THE OLIGOCHAETES AND LEECHES

IN THE preceding chapters we have discussed the origin and evolution of the polychaetes, and have described some of the ways in which the annelid body is organized and its activities co-ordinated. The origin and evolution of the oligochaetes and leeches remain to be considered.

Animals which have developed osmoregulatory mechanisms enabling them to live in fresh or almost fresh water are still faced with problems of reproduction, for while the adults may be able to cope with the environment, their gametes or larvae may not. A common solution is to adopt means of internal fertilization, followed by viviparous development or protection of large eggs which hatch at a late stage of development. A first step towards the oligochaetes of today may be imagined as an assumption of some means of transference of sperm to spermathecae of another worm. The stored sperm then fertilized the eggs later when these were laid. The eggs would be large so that hatching was delayed, and they may have been protected with mucus or other substances secreted at the time of fertilization forming a simple capsule. A cocoon secreted by a distinct clitellum may have evolved gradually in adaptation to swamps or lake margins subject to drying. Worms able to survive such periods of drought presumably gave rise to the earthworms we know today. This event probably did not occur before the Cretaceous, when the angiosperms, which largely contribute the humus on which earthworms depend, arose. Indeed, the evolution of soil itself is partly due to earthworm action. The earthworms of today are probably derived from genera of Tertiary or Quaternary age, a view supported by their geographical distribution.

Oliogochaetes

The arrangement of the genital segments and the gonoducts, of which the broad features were described in the preceding chapter, forms the basis of classification of the oligochaetes, for the arrangement of these organs is relatively constant in each family. The lumbriculids are rather exceptional in this respect. Michaelsen divided all the oligochaetes into four orders according to the position of the opening of the vasa deferentia in relation to the testes, and to the relative position of these to the spermathecae (fig. 19).[67] The Plesiopora include those worms in which the vasa deferentia open on the segment following that containing the testes. There are two groups of plesiopores: the plesiothecous—those in which the spermathecae are found in the same segment or near the segments containing the testes—and the prosothecous plesiopores, in which the spermathecae are situated far anterior to the genital segments. The tubificids and naidids are included in the first order (plesiothecous plesiopores), the enchytraeids in the second (prosothecous plesiopores). The third order, the Prosopora, include the lumbriculids, which, as noted already, have the vasa deferentia opening in the same segment as that in which the testes lie. The parasitic leech-like branchiobdellids also belong to the Prosopora. The earthworms differ in having the vasa deferentia opening farther back, and they are all included in the fourth order or Opisthopora. The haplotaxids are intermediate in being plesioporous, but are commonly included within the Opisthopora for in other ways they show many resemblances to earthworms.

The aelosomatids are all small aquatic worms rarely resorting to sexual means of reproduction. Where known, the gonads seem specialized, and the clitellum restricted to the ventral side. There are no gonoducts and the nephridia apparently serve for this purpose. Like all the plesiothecous plesiopores, the aelosomatids have bundles of dorsal and ventral chaetae, and may be mistaken for polychaetes. Unlike aelosomatids, the segmentation of naidids and the

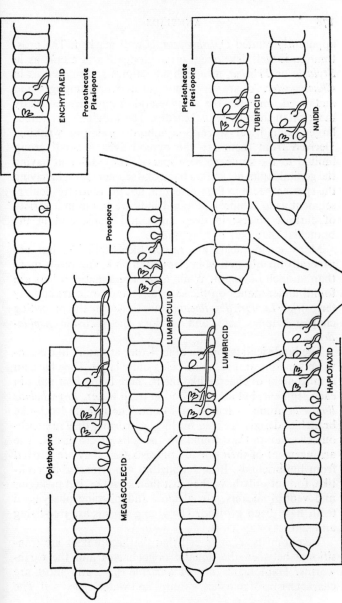

FIG. 19. The arrangement of the reproductive organs and the inter-relationships of the orders of Oligochaeta

apparently related *Opisthocysta*, is well marked. The prostomium is well developed, often elongate and tactile as in
Stylaria or *Pristina*, although sometimes snub-nosed as in
Chaetogaster. All are very small worms found amongst mud
and weed, and like the aelosomatids reproduce asexually
more often than by sexual means. The tubificids are rather
larger, cylindrical worms, commonly red and writhing.
Derived from them are the phreodrilids, a small group
limited to the southern hemisphere. They differ in having
the genital segments shifted back one segment, and in having
the spermathecae in the thirteenth, not the tenth (testicular)
segment as in tubificids. Phreodrilids are found in a variety
of curious places; in deep lakes and wells, and in the
branchial chambers of crayfishes.

Many enchytraeids are rather like tubificids, but are
generally opaque and white, less often pink, and rarely more
than an inch in length. While many are aquatic, others are
found under stones on the sea-shore, and some are entirely
terrestrial. *Lumbricillus lineatus* mentioned in the preceding
chapter belongs here, and so does the parasitic *Aspidodrilus*.

The lumbriculids, on the other hand, are more like earthworms in appearance, some being quite large. They have an
arrangement of chaetae like them, there being four pairs in
each segment, but all are found in fresh water. *Rhynchelmis
limosella* attains a length of 14 cm. The minute leech-like
branchiobdellids are also freshwater worms; they are without chaetae and are found on the gills of crayfishes. The
arrangement of their gonads suggests that they are derived
from lumbriculids. Branchiobdellids are remarkably leech-
like, for not only have they lost their chaetae, but posterior
and ventral suckers, dorsal anus and piercing pharyngeal
teeth have been evolved. The young worms are free-living
and subsist on detritus.

Taxonomists seem agreed that the haplotaxids are tran-
sitional between the aquatic oligochaetes and the earthworms. Haplotaxids are of variable size, and most are
characteristic of marshes, swamps and waterlogged soil. The

African *Allurodes* is separated as a distinct family as the arrangement of the genital organs is slightly different, while the African *Syngenodrilus* and the moniligastrids are other groups probably derived before the main families of earthworms were evolved. The moniligastrids include some giant earthworms found in southwest Asia, India and Japan; some *Drawida* attain 3–4 ft. in length, but are not as large as some glossoscolecids or megascolecids which can attain a length of 6 to 7 ft or more; Australian *Megascolides* have been found up to 11 ft in length, though these are exceptionally well-grown specimens, or were stretched when measured.

The majority of earthworms fall into one of four families, of which the Lumbricidae, including our own *Lumbricus*, *Allolobophora* and *Eisenia*, is one. The others are the Glossoscolecidae and Megascolecidae just mentioned, and the Eudrilidae. The members of all four families have testes in the tenth and/or eleventh segments of the body, with ovaries in the thirteenth segment. The glossoscolecids are distinguished by their lack of dorsal pores and by the usually multiple gizzard which extends back through the genital segments. The megascolecids and eudrilids are rather different from them; their chaetae are often multiplied and in some genera may even form a ring round each segment. They also have extensive prostatic glands. It is in these groups that worms with elaborate nephridial systems described in chapter 1 belong. The eudrilids are a small family found in Africa; interesting in having spermathecae closely associated with the openings of the oviducts. Most megascolecids are found in the southern hemisphere, southwest Asia and in the warmer parts of North America. Some are small, some adapted to the contrasting wet and dry seasons of monsoon lands, others to such specialized habitats as the reservoirs of bromelias and the humus in the leaf axils of tropical forest trees. Some of the speciation which has occurred in recent times amongst lumbricids is due to the formation of polyploids.

While the radiation of the families of earthworms from a

haplotaxid-like ancestor seems fairly clear, the status of the families of aquatic oligochaetes is less easy to define. The common division of the Oligochaeta into the Microdrili or Limicoles (the aquatic families) and the Megadrili or Terricoles (the earthworms) is mainly one of convenience. Stephenson[148] regarded the lumbriculids as the most primitive of the oligochaetes alive today, from which all others have been derived. He pointed out that they alone have the openings of the vasa deferentia in the same segment as the testes, a condition surely more primitive than those in which the ducts open more posteriorly. On the other hand, the arrangement of the genital segments is variable in lumbriculids, and as Avel[67] has pointed out, they are restricted to the northern hemisphere, and their chaetae are of the simple lumbricine type; characteristics unlikely to occur in an ancestral family. It also seems improbable that the freshwater aelosomatids and naidids, specialized as these families are in other ways, have been derived from them. Michaelsen,[67] on the other hand, proposed that the aeloso-matids were closest to the stock from which all other oligochaetes have been derived, and whilst recognizing the many specializations they show, suggested that from this stock the naidids and tubificids were evolved before the lumbriculids appeared. Stephenson[148] was inclined to attribute the evolution of copulation and of the clitellum to an adaptation to a terrestrial or semi-terrestrial environment. It is difficult to decide how far the evolution of copu-latory mechanisms and egg protection was related to adaptation to fresh water, or to more specialized habitats subject to periodic drought. Drying pools could have led to intolerable conditions prompting a more terrestrial life and aerial respiration, and to protection of the young by cocoon formation secreted by a clitellum. It was a relatively simple step for a worm with a cylindrical body adapted for burrowing in the marginal mud of swamps subject to drought to become truly terrestrial once a protective cocoon had been evolved. The aelosomatids and naidids are perhaps best regarded as specialized offshoots of the annelid stock which gave rise to such worms after their adaptation to fresh water. The tubificids and enchytraeids were derived later, while from the more terrestrial lumbriculids some secondarily aquatic worms have been evolved.

A classification of the Oligochaeta following that of Avel[67] and including all the genera mentioned in these pages is given in the Appendix. British oligochaetes may be identified with the aid of Brinkhurst.[18]

Leeches

The leeches are clitellate when breeding and are manifestly derived from some oligochaete ancestor. Most leeches are free-living and remain attached to their hosts only whilst feeding; they are no more parasites than lampreys. A few, however, stay on their hosts almost indefinitely once they have got there. *Calliobdella lophii* on angler fish and *Theromyzon* found in the nasal passages of certain water birds are examples of leeches which are really parasitic.

One curious fact about leeches is that they all have a body composed of 33 segments, although this is far from obvious owing to a variable number of secondary annulations. Most of the characters of leeches have been discussed already. It will be recalled that all have a ventral sucker formed from the last six segments of the body, and that this adheres by a combination of mucus and suction caused by concentric muscles formed from the circular muscles of the segments from which the sucker is derived. The smaller sucker round the mouth is more varied in development. Like the earthworms the leeches are cross-fertilizing hermaphrodites.

In the rivers of northwest Russia and Finland, salmon are found with a curious little worm which seems to combine these characters of the leeches with those of the oligochaetes. This is *Acanthobdella peledina*, as near a perfect link between the two classes as any taxonomist could wish to find. The body is composed of only 30 segments, however, each divided into four annuli, the last four segments being modified to act as a sucker and the rectum opening subterminally at a dorsal anus. The coelomic spaces, though reduced by the growth of connective tissue, are separated by septa as in oligochaetes; the gut is simpler than in leeches, and there are four pairs of short lumbricine chaetae in segments 4–6.

Acanthobdella peledina is an isolated species often placed in an order of its own. A number of other leech-like oligochaetes such as *Aspidodrilus* and the branchiobdellids are known, but none of these lie near the stock from which the Hirudinea evolved. Wendrowsky's counting of the chromosomes of different leech genera confirms the suggestion that *Acanthobdella* lies near the base of leech evolution. He found it to have a diploid number of 16 in common with some glossiphoniids.[108]

Of the origin of the leeches from the Oligochaeta there can be no doubt, but it is less easy to point to any oligochaete family as ancestral. Michaelsen drew attention to the lumbriculid *Agriodrilus vermivorous* found in Lake Baikal which has well-developed pharyngeal muscles reminiscent of those of leeches and a coelom somewhat restricted by the ingrowth of connective tissue, but these resemblances are probably due to parallel evolution. It seems likely that the leeches did not diverge from the Oligochaeta before the clitellum had become well established, although Schmidt[138] considers the habit of secretion of a protective cocoon to have evolved independently in the oligochaetes and in the leeches. It is not surprising, then, to find that the leeches resemble the haplotaxids more closely than other oligochaetes, a group nearest the stock from which the earthworms were also derived.

Apart from *Acanthobdella*, all the leeches we know may be assigned to one of three orders. These are the Rhynchobdellae, comprising leeches with an eversible proboscis, the Gnathobdellae, including leeches like the medicinal leech and horse leech which have cutting pharyngeal teeth, and the Pharyngobdellae which have a sucking pharynx like that of gnathobdelliforms, but from which the teeth are absent.

The rhynchobdelliform leeches include two families: the Glossiphoniidae, which are generally somewhat flattened leeches with a rather poorly developed anterior sucker, and the Piscicolidae or Ichthyobdellidae, which have more cylindrical bodies and usually well-marked anterior suckers which are often circular and almost as large as the disc-shaped posterior ones. The glossiphoniids are a freshwater group and different species may be found on all kinds of animals from crayfish to hippopotami. While many piscicolids are freshwater animals, others are found in the sea; and as their name implies they mainly attack fish. *Pontobdella* found on skates and rays, and *Piscicola* on various freshwater fishes, are probably the most familiar, but some others are found on shrimps and other crustaceans. In some piscicolids the body is somewhat constricted into two regions, and it is to this family that most of those leeches with gills or prominent papillae belong. *Ozobranchus* is one of the best known of these with large tufted gills on each side of the middle of the body. One African species is commonly found in the mouths of crocodiles or pelicans; another, mentioned earlier, on turtles.

The Gnathobdellae also comprise two main families, of which the Hirudidae including the medicinal and horse leeches is one. The other main family is the Haemadipsidae, an exclusively tropical and subtropical group of more or less terrestrial leeches which hang from foliage in wet forests and attach themselves to passing mammals, including man when available.[146] The majority are found in the Indomalayan region and in Japan, but they occur in parts of Australia, Madagascar and Chile. The leeches of both families have three serrate pharyngeal teeth, and are very similar in structure. In a third, minor, family, the Semiscolecidae, the jaws are reduced to a median dorsal rudiment.

The Pharyngobdellae have six to eight pairs of eyes, as compared with five pairs in gnathobdelliform leeches, and include three related families and two others of rather more doubtful affinity. The most important family is the

Erpobdellidae of which some species of *Erpobdella* itself are common freshwater leeches in this country, feeding on molluscs, planarians, *Chironomus* larvae and the like. *Odontobdella* and *Trocheta*, two leeches preying mainly on earthworms, and therefore found in moist soil near ponds and streams, also belong here. The trematobdellids are rather similar, but African and Indomalayan in distribution. *Americobdella valdiviana* of Chile is a terrestrial leech and probably the largest ever found—between 6 in. and 1 ft in length, according to how stretched it is. Caballero[67] places it with the Pharyngobdellae, but perhaps it is nearer the haemadipsids and hirudids; Mann[108] includes it in the latter family.

British leeches can be identified with the aid of Mann.[108] A classification of the leeches, together with the genera mentioned in this book, is given in the Appendix.

APPENDIX

Classification of the Phylum Annelida, including the names of the genera mentioned in this book. Families of uncertain position are placed in brackets.

CLASS ARCHIANNELIDA

Polygordius, Protodrilus, Saccocirrus, Nerilla, Dinophilus

CLASS POLYCHAETA

ORDER PHYLLODOCIDA

Family 1 Phyllodocidae
          2 Alciopidae
          3 Tomopteridae
          4 Typhloscolecidae
          5 Aphroditidae, *in sensu lato*: *Aphrodite, Hermione, Halosydna, Gattyana, Arctonoë, Harmothoë, Euthalenessa*
          6 Chrysopetalidae, including Palmyridae
          7 Glyceridae: *Glycera*
          8 Goniadidae
          9 Sphaerodoridae
       10 Pisionidae: *Pisione*
       11 Nephthyidae: *Nephthys*
       12 Syllidae: *Calamyzas, Syllis, Odontosyllis, Procerastea, Autolytus, Myrianida, Trypanosyllis, Eusyllis, Exogone, Sphaerosyllis, Pionosyllis, Parapionosyllis, Typosyllis*
       13 Hesionidae: *Irma, Ophiodromus, Hesione*
       14 Pilargiidae
       15 Nereidae: *Nereis, Perinereis, Tyllorhynchus, Platynereis, Lycastis*

ORDER CAPITELLIDA
Family 1 Capitellidae: *Capitella*
     2 Arenicolidae: *Arenicola*
     3 Scalibregmidae: *Scalibregma*
     4 Maldanidae: *Clymenella, Axiothella*
     5 Opheliidae: *Ophelia, Thoracophelia, Travisia*

ORDER STERNASPIDA
Family 1 Sternaspidae: *Sternaspis*

ORDER SPIONIDA
Family 1 Spionidae: *Polydora, Pygospio, Scolelepis*
     2 Disomidae
     3 Poecilochaetidae: *Poecilochaetus*
     4 Longosomidae
     5 Paraonidae
     6 (Opisthabranchidae)
     7 Chaetopteridae: *Chaetopterus, Ranzania, Phyllo-chaetopterus*
     8 Sabellariidae: *Sabellaria, Phalacrostemma*

ORDER EUNICIDA=Eunicidae *in sensu lato*
Family 1 Onuphidae: *Hyalinoecia*
     2 Eunicidae: *Marphysa, Eunice, Lysidice*
     3 Lumbrinereidae: *Haematocleptes*
     4 Arabellidae: *Oligognathus*
     5 Lysaretidae: *Halla*
     6 Dorvilleidae: *Ophryotrocha*
     7 Histriobdellidae: *Histriobdella*
     8 (Ichthyotomidae): *Ichthyotomus*

ORDER AMPHINOMIDA
Family Amphinomidae *in sensu lato*

ORDER MAGELONIDA
Family Magelonidae: *Magelona*

ORDER ARICIIDA
Family Ariciidae: *Scoloplos*

ORDER CIRRATULIDA
Family 1 Cirratulidae: *Dodecaceria*
     2 Ctenodrilidae: *Ctenodrilus*
     3 (Stygocapitellidae)

ORDER OWENIIDA
    Family   Oweniidae: *Owenia, Myriochele*

ORDER TEREBELLIDA
    Family 1 Pectinariidae = Amphictenidae: *Pectinaria*
         2 Ampharetidae: *Amphicteis*
         3 Terebellidae: *Polycirrus, Lanice, Amphitrite, Terebella, Thelepus, Loimia, Eupolymnia*

ORDER FLABELLIGERIDA
    Family   Flabelligeridae = Chloraemidae

ORDER PSAMMODRILIDA
    Family   Psammodrilidae

ORDER SABELLIDA
    Family 1 Sabellidae: *Fabricia, Sabella, Schizobranchia, Bispira, Myxicola, Branchiomma, Eudistylia, Dybowscella, Manayunkia*
         2 Serpulidae: *Pomatoceros, Spirorbis, Salmacina, Serpula, Hydroides, Filograna, Microserpula, Vermiliopsis, Apomatus*

CLASS MYZOSTOMARIA

Myzostomum, Protomyzostomum

CLASS OLIGOCHAETA

ORDER PLESIOPORA PLESIOTHECATA
    Family 1 Aelosomatidae: *Aelosoma*
         2 Naididae: *Nais, Stylaria, Aulophorus, Pristina, Chaetogaster*
         3 Opisthocystidae: *Opisthocysta*
         4 Tubificidae: *Tubifex, Branchiura, Bothrioneurium*
         5 Phreodrilidae

ORDER PLESIOPORA PROSOTHECATA
    Family   Enchytraeidae: *Aspidodrilus, Lumbricillus, Pelmatodrilus, Enchytraeus*

ORDER PROSOPORA
    Family 1 Lumbriculidae: *Agriodrilus, Lumbriculus, Rhynchelmis*
         2 Branchiobdellidae

ORDER OPISTHOPORA
Family 1 Haplotaxidae = Phreocytidae
     2 Allurodidae: *Allurodes*
     3 Syngenodrilidae: *Syngenodrilus*
     4 Moniligastridae: *Drawida*
     5 Glossoscolecidae: *Thamnodrilus, Alma, Glossoscolex Pontoscolex, Andiodrilus, Criodrilus*
     6 Lumbricidae: *Lumbricus, Eisenia, Allolobophora*
     7 Megascolecidae: *Pheretima, Hoplochaetella, Eutyphoeus, Chilota, Megascolex, Tonoscolex, Microscolex, Perionyx, Megascolides*
     8 Eudrilidae: *Malodrilus*

CLASS HIRUDINEA

ORDER ACANTHOBDELLAE
Family   Acanthobdellidae: *Acanthobdella*

ORDER RHYNCHOBDELLAE
Family 1 Glossiphoniidae: *Placobdella, Hemiclepsis, Helobdella, Glossiphonia, Theromyzon*
     2 Piscicolidae = Ichthyobdellidae: *Piscicola, Calliobdella, Hemibdella, Branchellion, Pontobdella, Ozobranchus*

ORDER GNATHOBDELLAE
Family 1 Hirudidae: *Haemopis, Poecilobdella* (= *Hirudinaria*), (*Americobdella*)
     2 Haemadipsidae: *Haemadipsa*
     3 Semiscolecidae

ORDER PHARYNGOBDELLAE
Family 1 Erpobdellidae: *Erpobdella* (= *Herpobdella*), *Odontobdella, Trocheta*
     2 Trematobdellidae

REFERENCES

References not given below are to be found in the papers quoted.

**Denotes a paper or a work with comprehensive bibliography.*

1   Abdel-Fattah, R. F. (1955) *Proc. Egypt. Acad. Sci.*, **10**, 36

2   Abeloos, M. (1955) *Bull. Soc. zool. Fr.*, **80**, 228

3   Alsterberg, G. (1922) *Acta. Univ. lund.*, (2) **18**, 1

4   Anderson, D. T. (1959) *Quart. J. micr. Sci.*, **100**, 89

5   Bahl, K. N. (1927), *Quart. J. micr. Sci.*, **71**, 479

*6 Bahl, K. N. (1947) *Biol. Rev.*, **22**, 109

7   Beadle, L. C. (1931) *J. exp. Biol.*, **8**, 211

8   Beadle, L. C. (1937) *J. exp. Biol.*, **14**, 56

9   Beadle, L. C. (1957) *ibid.*, **34**, 1

*10 Berrill, N. J. (1952) *Biol. Rev.*, **27**, 401

11 Bevelander, G. and Nakahara, I. (1959) *Physiol. Zool.*, **32**, 40

*12 Bobin, G. (1944) *Ann. Inst. océanogr., Monaco*, **22**, 1

13 Bobin, G. and Mazoué, H. (1944) *Bull. Soc. zool. Fr.*, **69**, 125

14 Bonhomme, C. (1954) *Arch. Anat. micr. Morph, exp.*, **43**, 202

15 Bradbury, S. (1959) *Quart. J. micr. Sci.*, **100**, 325

16 Brand, T. F. von (1946) Anaerobiosis in invertebrates, *Biodynamica Monographs*, No. 4

17 Brasil, M. L. (1904) *Arch. Zool. exp. gén.* (4) **2**, 91

18 Brinkhurst, R. O. (1963) *Freshw. biol. Ass. Sci. Publ., in press.*

19 Brumpt, E. (1900) *Mém. Soc. zool. Fr.*, **13**, 286

20 Bullock, T. H. (1948) *Physiol. comp.*, **1**, 1

21 Büsing, K. H., Döll, W. and Freytag, K. (1953) *Arch. Mikrobiol.*, **19**, 52

*22 Chapman, G. (1958) *Biol. Rev.*, **33**, 338

23 Clark, R. B. (1956) *Quart. J. micr. Sci.*, **97**, 235

24 Clark, R. B. (1958) *Zool. Jb., Abt. 3*, **68**, 261

25 Clark, R. B. (1959) *Anim. Behaviour*, **7**, 85

*26 Clark, R. B. (1961) *Biol. Rev.*, **36**, 199

27 Clark, R. B. and Clark, M. E. (1960) *Quart J. micr. Sci.*, **101**, 149

28 Clark, R. B. and Clark, M. E. (1960) *ibid.*, **101**, 133

29 Clark, R. B. and Evans, S. M. (1961) *J. Embryol. exp. Morph.*, **9**, 97

30 Collier, H. O. J. (1939) *J. exp. Biol.*, **16**, 300

31 Cresp, J. (1956) *Bull. Soc. zool. Fr.*, **81**, 183

32 Dales, R. P. (1952) *Quart. J. micr. Sci.*, **93**, 435

33 Dales, R. P. (1955) *J. mar. biol. Ass. U.K.*, **34**, 55

34 Dales, R. P. (1957) *J. mar. biol. Ass. U.K.*, **36**, 81

35 Dales, R. P. (1957) *ibid.*, **36**, 309

36 Dales, R. P. (1958) *ibid.*, **37**, 521

37 Dales, R. P. (1961) *Biol. Bull.*, **121**, 82

38 Dales, R. P. (1961) *Physiol. Zool.*, **34**, 306

39 Dales, R. P. (1961) *Quart. J. micr. Sci.*, **102**, 327

40 Dales, R. P. (1962) *Proc. zool. Soc. Lond.*, **139**, 389

41 Dam, L. van (1940) *J. exp. Biol.*, **17**, 1

42 Darboux, J. G. (1899) *Bull. sci. Fr. Belg.*, **33**, 1

43 Dasgupta, A. S. and Austin, A. P. (1960) *Quart. J. micr. Sci.*, **101**, 395

44 Dausend, K. (1931) *Z. vergl. Physiol.*, **14**, 557

45 Davenport, D., Camougis, G. and Hickok, J. F. (1960) *Anim. Behav.*, **8**, 209

46 Durchon, M. (1952) *Arch. Zool. exp. gén.*, **88**, 96

*47 Durchon, M. (1952) *Ann. Sci. nat.*, **14**, 119

48 Durchon, M. (1956) *Ann. Sci. nat.*, **18**, 1

49 Durchon, M. (1959) *Bull. biol.*, **93**, 155

*50 Durchon, M. (1960) *Bull. Soc. zool. Fr.*, **85**, 275

51 Ebling, F. J. (1945) *Quart. J. micr. Sci.*, **85**, 153

52 Eliassen, E. (1955) *Univ. Bergen Årb. naturv. R.*, No. 12, 1

53 Ellis, W. G. (1937) *J. exp. Biol.*, **14**, 340

54 Ewer, D. W. (1941) *Quart. J. micr. Sci.*, **82**, 587

*55 Fauvel, P. (1923, 1927) *Faune de France*, **5**, **16**

56 Fordham, M. G. C. (1925) L.M.B.C. Memoir No. 27, Univ. Liverpool

57 Fox, H. M. (1932) *Proc. roy. Soc.*, B., **111**, 356

58 Fox, H. M. (1938) *ibid.*, **125**, 554

59 Friedländer, B. (1894) *Pflüg. Arch. ges. Physiol.*, **58**, 168

60 Fretter, V. (1955) *J. mar. biol. Ass. U.K.*, **34**, 151

61 Gansen, P. Semal-van (1957) *Bull. biol.*, **90**, 335

62 Gansen, P. Semal-van (1957) *ibid.*, **91**, 226

63 Gansen, P. Semal-van (1959) *Ann. Soc. zool. Belg.*, **89**, 341

64   Gansen, P. Semal-van and Vandermeerssche, G. (1958) *Bull. micr. Appl.*, **8**, 7

65   Gilpin-Brown, J. B. (1958) *J. comp. Neurol.*, **109**, 317

*66 Goodrich, E. S. (1946) *Quart. J. micr. Sci.*, **86**, 113

*67 Grassé, P.-P. (1959) *Traité de Zoologie*, **5** (1)

68   Gravier, C. (1923) *Ann. Sci. nat.*, (10) **6**, 153

69   Gray, J. (1939) *J. exp. Biol.*, **16**, 9

70   Gray, J. and Lissman, H. W. (1938). *J. exp. Biol.*, **15**, 518

71   Gray, J., Lissman, H. W. and Pumphrey, R. J. (1938) *ibid.*, **15**, 408

72   Grove, A. J., and Cowley, L. F. (1926) *Quart. J. micr. Sci.*, **70**, 559

*73 Hanson, J. (1949) *Biol. Rev.*, **24**, 127

74   Hanson, J. (1951) *Quart. J. micr. Sci.*, **92**, 377

75   Hanström, B. (1927) *Z. Morph. Ökol. Tiere*, **7**, 543

76   Hauenschild, C. (1956) *Z. Naturw.*, **11b**, 610

77   Hauenschild, C. (1956) *Naturwissenschaften*, **16**, 361

78   Hedley, R. H. (1958) *J. mar. biol. Ass. U. K.*, **37**, 315

79   Hempel, C. (1957) *Helgoländ wiss. Meeresunters.*, **6**, 100

80   Herlant-Meewis, H. (1947) *Ann. Soc. zool. Belg.*, **77**, 5

81   Herlant-Meewis, H. (1953) *ibid.*, **84**, 117

82   Herlant-Meewis, H. (1954) *Arch. Biol.*, *Paris*, **65**, 73

*83 Herlant-Meewis, H. (1958) *Ann. biol.*, *Copenhague*, **34**, 133

84   Herlant-Meewis, H. (1959) *Ann. Soc. zool. Belg.*, **89**, 281

84a Herlant-Meewis, H. (1961) *Bull. biol.*, **95**, 695

85   Hess, W. N. (1925) *J. Morph.*, **41**, 63

86   Hesse, R. (1899) *Z. wiss. Zool.*, **65**, 446

87   Horridge, G. A. (1959) *Proc. roy. Soc.*, B, **150**, 245

88   Jägersten, G. (1940) *Vidensk. Medd. dansk. naturh. Foren. Kbh.*, **104**, 103

89   Johnson, F. H. and Johnson, M. W. (1959) *J. cell. comp. Physiol.*, **53**, 179

90   Johnson, M. L. (1942) *J. exp. Biol.*, **18**, 266

91   Jones, J. D. (1954) *J. exp. Biol.*, **32**, 110

92   Jørgensen, C. B. and Dales, R. P. (1957) *Physiol. comp.*, **4**, 357

93   Jürgens, O. (1935) *Zool. Jb.*, *Abt. 3*, **55**, 1

94   Kaiser, F. (1954) *Zool. Jb.*, *Abt. 3*, **65**, 59

95   Kennedy, G. Y. and Dales, R. P. (1958) *J. mar. biol. Ass. U.K.*, **37**, 15

96   Kennedy, G. Y. and Nicol, J. A. C. (1960) *Proc. roy. Soc.*, B, **150**, 509

97 Kermack, D. M. (1953) *Proc. zool. Soc. Lond.*, **125**, 347
98 Korringa, P. (1957) in *Treatise on marine ecology and paleo-ecology*, Geol. Soc. Amer., **67** (1), 917
99 Krivanek, J. O. (1956) *Physiol. Zool.*, **29**, 241
99a Krüger, F. (1959) *Zool. Anz.*, **22** Suppl. Bd., 115
100 Langdon, F. E. (1900) *J. comp. Neurol.*, **10**, 1
100a Laverack, M. S. (1960) *Comp. Biochem. Physiol.*, **1**, 155
100b Laverack, M. S. (1961) *Comp. Biochem. Physiol.*, **2**, 22
101 Lindroth, A. (1938) *Zool. Bidr. Uppsala*, **17**, 367
101a Lotmar, W. and Picken, L. E. R. (1950) *Experientia*, **6**, 58
102 Ludwig, W. and Ludwig, H. W. (1954) *Arch. EntMech. Org.*, **147**, 259
103 McConnaughy, B. H. and Fox, D. L. (1949) *Univ. Calif. Publ. Zool.*, **47**, 319
104 McGinitie, G. E. (1939) *Biol. Bull.*, **77**, 115
105 McIntosh, W. C. (1900–23) *The British marine annelids*, London, Roy. Soc.
106 Malaquin A. (1893) *Recherches sur les Syllidiens*, Mém. Soc. Sci. Arts, Lille
107 Málek, R. (1927) *Biol. gen.*, **3**, 317
*108 Mann, K. M. (1962) *Leeches* (*Hirudinea*), London, Pergamon
109 Marcus, E. (1943) *Bol. Fac. Fil. Ciên. Letr. Univ. S. Paulo*, No. 32, 3
110 Mendes, E. G. and Nonato, E. F. (1957) *Bol. Fac. Fil. Ciên, Letr. Univ. S. Paulo*, No. 21, 153
111 Millott, N. (1943) *Proc. roy. Soc.*, B, **131**, 362
112 Myot, C. (1957) *Arch. Zool. exp. gén.*, **94**, 61
113 Needham, A. E. (1957) *J. exp. Biol.*, **34**, 425
114 Needham, A. E. (1960) *ibid.*, **37**, 775
115 Newell, G. E. (1950) *J. exp. Biol.*, **27**, 110
116 Nicol, E. A. T. (1930) *Trans. roy. Soc. Edinb.*, **56**, 537
*117 Nicol, J. A. C. (1948) *Quart. Rev. Biol.*, **23**, 291
118 Nicol, J. A. C. (1950) *J. mar. biol. Ass. U.K.*, **29**, 303
119 Nicol, J. A. C. (1951) *J. exp. Biol.*, **28**, 22
120 Nicol, J. A. C. (1954) *J. mar. biol. Ass. U.K.*, **33**, 177
121 Nicol, J. A. C. (1957) *ibid.*, **36**, 271
122 Nicol, J. A. C. and Whitteridge, D. (1955) *Physiol. comp.*, **4**, 101
123 Nicoll, P. A. (1954) *Biol. Bull.*, **106**, 69
124 Okada, Y. K. (1929) *Arch. EntMech. Org.*, **115**, 542
125 Okada, Y. K. (1934) *Bull. Soc. zool. Fr.*, **59**, 388

126 Potts, F. A. (1913) *Proc. Cambr. phil. Soc.*, **17**, 193

*127 Potts, W. T. W. and Parry, G. (1963) *Osmotic and Ionic regulation in animals*, London, Pergamon

128 Prosser, C. L. (1934) *J. comp. Neurol.*, **59**, 61

129 Prosser, C. L. (1935) *J. exp. Biol.*, **12**, 95

130 Prosser, C. L. (1950) *Biol. Bull.*, **98**, 254

131 Ralph, C. L. (1957) *Physiol. Zool.*, **30**, 41

132 Ramsay, J. A. (1949) *J. exp. Biol.*, **26**, 65

133 Robertson, J. D. (1935) *J. exp. Biol.*, **12**, 279

133a Roche, J., Bessis, M., Breton-Gorius, J., and Stralin, H. (1961) *C. R. Soc. biol.*, **155**, 1790

134 Roots, B. I. (1960) *Comp. Biochem. Physiol*, **1**, 218

*135 Rullier, F. (1950) *Ann. Inst. océanogr.*, *Monaco*, **23**, 207

136 Rushton, W. A. H. (1946) *Proc. roy. Soc.*, B, **133**, 109

137 Schlieper, C. (1929) *Z. vergl. Physiol.*, **9**, 478

138 Schmidt, G. A. (1944) *J. gen. Biol. Moscow*, **5**, 284

139 Sie, H.-C., Chang, J. J. and Johnson, F. H. (1958) *J. cell. comp. Physiol.*, **52**, 195

140 Singleton, L. (1957) *Biochim. biophys. Acta*, **24**, 67

141 Skowron, S. (1926) *Biol. Bull.*, **51**, 199

142 Smith, J. E. (1957) *Phil. Trans.*, B, **240**, 135

143 Smith, R. I. (1942) *Physiol. Zool.*, **15**, 410

144 Smith, R. I. (1956) *Ann. biol. Copenhague*, **33**, 93

145 Smith, R. I. (1959) *Marine biology*. 20th ann. biol. coloq. Oregon State Coll.

146 Stammers, F. M. G. (1950) *Parasitology*, **40**, 237

147 Stephan-Dubois, F. (1958) *Arch. Anat. micr. Morph. exp.*, **47**, 605

*148 Stephenson, J. (1930) *The Oligochaeta*, O.U.P.

149 Storch, O. (1913) *S. B. Akad. Wiss. Wien*, **122**, 1

150 Sutton, M. F. (1957) *Proc. zool. Soc. Lond.*, **129**, 487

151 Swan, E. F. (1950) *J. Morph.*, **86**, 285

152 Swedmark, B. (1959) *Ark. Zool.*, **12**, 55

153 Thouveny, Y. (1958) *Bull. Soc. zool. Fr.*, **83**, 107

154 Unteutsch, W. (1937) *Zool. Jb.*, *Abt. 3*, **58**, 69

155 Ullman, A. and Bookhout, C. G. (1949) *J. Morph.*, **84**, 31

156 Urich, K. (1958) *Z. wiss. Physiol.*, **41**, 342

157 Vannini, E. and Ranzoli, F. (1957) *Pubbl. Staz. zool. Napoli*, **30**, 210

158 Watson, A. T. (1928) *Proc. Liverpool biol. Soc.*, **42**, 25

159 Watson, M. R. (1958) *Biochem. J.*, **68**, 416

160 Wells, G. P. (1937) *J. exp. Biol.*, **14**, 117

161   Wells, G. P. (1945) *J. mar. biol. Ass. U. K.*, **26**, 170
*162   Wells, G. P. (1950) *Soc. exp. Biol.*, *Symposium*, **4**, 127
163   Wells, G. P. (1951) *Proc. roy. Soc.*, B, **138**, 278
164   Wells, G. P. (1952) *Proc. roy. Soc.*, B, **140**, 70
165   Wells, G. P. (1953) *J. mar. biol. Ass. U.K.*, **32**, 51
166   Wells, G. P. (1954) *Quart. J. micr. Sci.*, **95**, 251
167   Wells, G. P. and Dales, R. P. (1951) *J. mar. biol. Ass. U.K.*, **29**, 661
168   Wells, G. P. and Ledingham, I. (1940) *J. exp. Biol.*, **17**, 353
169   Whitear, M. (1953) *Quart. J. micr. Sci.*, **94**, 293
170   Wilson, D. M. (1960) *J. exp. Biol.*, **37**, 46
171   Wilson, D. P. (1932) *Phil. Trans.*, B, **221**, 231
*172   Wilson, D. P. (1952) *Ann. océanogr.*, *Monaco*, **27**, 49
173   Wolf, A. V. (1940) *Physiol. Zool.*, **13**, 294
174   Woltereck, R. (1902) *Zoologica*, *Leipzig*, **13**, Hft. 34
175   Wu, K. S. (1939) *J. exp. Biol.*, **16**, 251
176   Yerkes, R. M. (1912) *J. Anim. Behav.*, **2**, 332
177   Zoond, A. (1931) *J. exp. Biol.*, **8**, 258

INDEX

Figures in heavy type refer to illustrations

piscicolids, 16, 183; nephridia, 34; reproduction, 173, 174
Pisione, reproduction, 170
pisionids, 74
Placobdella, colour, 139; gut, 61; vessels, 85
planktotrophic larvae, 171
Platynereis, metamorphosis, 165–7; swarming, 168, 169
Plesiopora, 176
Poecilobdella, **20**; nephridia, 34; sinus system, **86**
Poecilochaetus, 71
polybostrichus, 164
Polychaeta, 11; classification, 185; estuarine-, 106; evolution, 64–76; family relationships, **75**; identification, 76; proboscis, **44**
Polycirrus, blood system, 98; corpuscles, 89; feeding, 48; luminescence, 141
Polydora, 71; regeneration, 154
Polygordius, 65; larval metamorphosis, 27, 171
polynoids, **73**
polyploids, 179
Pomatoceros, chromosomes, 169; feeding, 53; gut, 57; larvae, 171
Pontobdella, 183
Pontoscolex, respiration, 97
predators, 16, 58
pre-oral sacs, 25–6
presegmental region, 25, 27; see prostomium
Pristina, prostomium, 178
proboscis, glossoscolecid, 144; polychaete, 41, 42–6, **44**, 65, 69, 70, 71, 72, 76
Procerastea, regeneration, 152; respiration, 158
proctodeum, 41
Prosopora, 176
Prosothecata, 176
prostomium, 13, 16, 17, 25, 48, 68; eyes, 139; in regeneration, 155, 156; sense organs, 136, 144
Protodrilus, 65
Protomyzostomum, 62
protonephridia, 29, 74
protonephromixia, 30, 74
prototroch, 26
proventriculus, 166
psammodrilids, 68
Pseudomonas, 61
pygidial budding, 161–2
pygidium, 17, 25, 28–9, 137, 143
Pygospio, reproduction, 158

R

ragworms, 12, 19; see *Nereis*
Ranzania, 71; eyes, 138
receptacula seminis, 170
regeneration, 152–7
reproduction, asexual, 158–62; sexual, 162–70
Rhynchelmis, 178; regeneration, 157
rhynchobdellids, 182; proboscis, 42, 60; reproduction, 173
rhythms, in behaviour, 131–2, 146–7;

locomotion, 130; muscles, 127, 129, 132; nerve cord, 127, 130–1
rockworms, 14; see *Marphysa*

S

Sabella, behaviour, 140, 145; blood, 90; coelomocytes, 103; feeding, 52–3, 57; irrigation, 95–96; nerve cord, 115; regeneration, 155, 156; reproduction, 158; respiration, 95; tubes, 94
sabellariids, **67**, 71, 72; development, 137, 171; feeding, 50
sabellids, 15, 64, 68; behaviour, 147; feeding, 51–2; nephridia, 32; regeneration, 153; respiration, 95; statocysts, 145; see *Sabella*, *Schizobranchia*, *Branchiomma*, *Myxicola*
Saccocirrus, 65
Sacconereis, 164
salivary glands, leech, 60; oligochaet, 58
sand-eating, 46–7, 55, 71
sand mason, 147; see *Lanice*
scales, 170; and luminescence, 142, 143
scaleworms, 14, 74; brood-care, 170; gut, 42
Scalibregma, 70; feeding, 47; proboscis, 43, 46
Schizobranchia, crown, 53; irrigation, 95–6; peritoneum, 103
schizogony, 161
scissiparity, 161
Scolelepis, 71
Scoloplos, development, 26; egg capsules, 170
sea mice, 14; see *Aphrodite*
Sedentaria, 13, 64
sedentary life, 48
segmental ducts, 17
segments, 13, 17, 19, 21; of leeches, 181; muscles, 123–5; number, 152
self-fertilization, 169
seminal vesicles, 170; in alciopids, 30
semiscolecids, 183
sense organs, 136–51
septa, 21, 24, 32, 36, 85
Serpula, blood, 90; pre-oral sacs, 25
serpulids, 15, 64, **67**, 68; feeding, 52; regeneration, 153
sex, 169
sexual reproduction, 162–9
shadow-reflex, 116, 118, 140, 148
sinus system, 86; in *Poecilobdella*, **86**
solenocytes, 29
spawning behaviour, 167–9
spermathecae, in classification, 176; of earthworm, 172
spermatophores, 173
sphaerodorids, 74
Sphaerosyllis, reproduction, 170
sphincters, 35–6
spintherids, 69
Spionida, 72
spionids, 71, 72; development, 171; feeding, 50; sense organs, 137
spiral cleavage, 22–4, **23**
spiral organs, 137
Spirographis, see *Sabella*
Spirorbis, reproduction, 170